T.A. WILLIAMS

Never too late

CANELO

First published in the United Kingdom in 2023 by

Canelo
Unit 9, 5th Floor
Cargo Works, 1–2 Hatfields
London SE1 9PG
United Kingdom

A CIP catalogue record for this book is available from the British Library.

Print ISBN 978 1 80436 241 9
Ebook ISBN 978 1 80436 240 2

Cover design by Diane Meacham

Look for more great books at www.canelo.co

Printed and bound in Great Britain by Clays Ltd, Elcograf S.p.A.

1

To Mariangela and Christina as always with love

Prologue

'What's this, Ethan?'

'What's what?' He didn't bother to look up from what he was doing at the back of one of the amplifiers.

'This little bag? What's it doing stuffed in here under the console?'

In an instant Steph had his full attention, and she couldn't miss the guilty look that passed across his face, immediately followed by that same petulant expression with which she had become increasingly familiar over the past months as he had started coming home late, often reeking of alcohol. Only this time it wasn't alcohol. The anonymous little plastic bag contained a white powder and she had a horrible feeling she knew what it was. She held it up and tried again, her voice heavy with sarcasm.

'Sugar maybe?'

'If you must know, it's talcum powder so my fingers don't slip on the sliders.' As usual he was trying to bluster his way out of it.

He dropped his eyes back to the recording console with its rows of lights, switches, knobs and sliders. He was deliberately avoiding looking at her but she knew how to be patient by now. She just stood there holding the little bag in the air until he finally raised his eyes again. After a year and a half of living together they both knew each other well enough for her to know he was lying and for him to realise that she knew. An expression of resignation appeared on his face.

'Yeah, all right, it's coke, but it's not mine.'

'There's cocaine here and you knew about it?' She raised her eyes in silent supplication towards the ceiling of the recording studio. 'We could be arrested just for possessing it. What on earth were you thinking? And if it isn't yours, whose is it?' She could feel her anger rising. His increasingly frequent late nights and excessive drinking had been bad enough, but now drugs?

'I can't say, but it's not mine.' He made a brave attempt to catch and hold her eye but his resolve barely lasted a second or two before he looked away. 'I'm telling you: it's not mine, Steph, honest.'

He had never been a good actor and Stephanie gave a sceptical snort.

'Just like the smell of booze coming off you last night was because Donny spilt his brandy on you?' She took a deep breath and stood there, wondering what to do. Things had been getting worse between them lately and she had the feeling that everything was leading inexorably towards her ending the relationship unless she could get him to turn over a new leaf. The trouble was that she had loved him. She still did when he wasn't playing at being a Jim Morrison or a Jimi Hendrix character, bent on self-destruction. However, if she were to dump him, this would also inevitably mean giving up the job she loved. After all, he owned the studio and at the end of the day she was his employee. Working for her ex, particularly after an acrimonious break-up, would be tough, if not impossible.

Music – of any kind – was in her blood and working here as a recording engineer was in so many ways her dream job. She was now on first name terms with many famous – and infamous – faces and had been actively involved in the production of a number of hit records. Giving that up would be hard, and she knew enough about the cut-throat world of the music industry to know that finding something similar wouldn't be easy. As for classical music, her first love, the opportunities were even more limited and worse paid.

Coming to a decision, she handed him the little bag. 'Here, take it. I'm tired of your lies, Ethan. Promise me you'll get rid of it now, this very minute. *I* don't want a criminal record, even if you do.'

She read relief on his face as he reached over and took the bag. 'Of course, Steph. I'll go out now and give it back to the guy.' Before she could question him any further he scuttled out of the door, leaving her sitting there questioning her life choices once more.

Chapter 1

The following week

'What did the doctor say?'

Steph could see that her mum was doing her best to sound casual but the anxiety in her voice was all too obvious.

'She told me it's definitely a lump, but she says it could easily be a harmless cyst.' Steph tried not to let her own fears spill out. Bursting into tears wouldn't do either of them any good.

Her mum even managed to produce an encouraging smile. 'So not dangerous. That's really good news, isn't it?'

Steph nodded dutifully. 'Hopefully it isn't anything sinister, but she's arranging for me to have a mammogram later this week just to be sure.' In fact the doctor hadn't actually pronounced any kind of judgement on Steph's lump, but there was no point in worrying her mum any more than necessary. 'If it's just a cyst, I expect they'll probably just leave well alone.'

'I'm sure it'll turn out to be nothing.' Her mum's tone became more downbeat. 'With your father they knew straightaway—' Steph cut in fast to interrupt what might become a morbid flow.

'It'll be fine, Mum. Try not to worry.'

'I'm not worried, darling. I'm sure it'll be fine, but it's always a good idea to get these things checked out.'

Steph could see how hard she was trying to sound optimistic and encouraging, and she loved her for it. She stood up, kissed her mum on the top of the head, and moved towards the kitchen. 'I feel like a cup of tea. Want some?' In fact, the way she had been feeling since coming out of the surgery, something a whole lot stronger held considerably more appeal, but she knew there was no booze at her mum's house.

'Yes, please, dear. But make mine weak or I won't sleep tonight.'

Steph glanced at her watch as she filled the kettle and raised her eyebrows. It was barely six.

'What did Ethan say when you told him?' Her mum's voice echoed in from the lounge.

Steph put on the kettle and returned to the lounge doorway. 'I haven't told him.'

'You haven't? No, I suppose it's best not to worry him until you know what's going on.'

Worry him? The way Ethan had been behaving recently, it probably wouldn't even have registered with him. 'Yes, best to wait.'

'There's cake in the tin. Mrs Edwards came around this afternoon, so I made a chocolate sponge.'

Steph made the tea, cut two slices of cake and returned to the lounge where the conversation soon revolved back to Ethan.

'How are things between the two of you? All going well?' From the tone of her mum's voice, Steph could tell that she knew full well that things weren't going swimmingly.

'Not really. He's being very immature.'

'Still staying out late? And what about his drinking?'

'Not getting any better, I'm afraid. The thing is, Mum, he wasn't like this when I first met him.'

Her mother surveyed her over the coffee table. Since moving in with Ethan eighteen months ago Steph had made a point of getting over to see her mum as often as she could as she knew how lonely it must be for her after the death of Steph's dad the previous year. The first few times she had brought Ethan with her, but her mother had never been keen on him and it was clear from her attitude today that she disapproved of him even more now.

'If you want my advice, Stephanie, you'd be much better off without him.' For a moment Steph waited for her to add, 'I told you so,' but she didn't.

'You may be right. I'm starting to think that myself.' Steph paused helplessly. 'It's just that if I leave him, I'll have to leave the studio.'

'You'll find something else. And surely your happiness is worth more than any job?'

'Yes, but much of my happiness *is* my job. I love it.'

'Why don't you look around to see what else is available before doing anything drastic? You never know what might come up. People move on, start families, get fired. Why not spend a few hours on the internet seeing what's available?' Her mum had always been a pragmatic sort of person.

Steph nodded in agreement. 'That's exactly what I was doing last night. The trouble is there's nothing here in London; at least, nothing as good as my present job.'

'Well, if you love it so much, you really need to sit down and talk to Ethan, tell him how you feel. Maybe he doesn't realise how his behaviour's affecting you.'

Steph sighed glumly. 'You're right. It's just that I'm not sure he's ready to modify his behaviour. The more time he spends with his mates – and there are some really wild ones among them – the worse he gets. Although he's thirty-six, he sometimes acts more like a sixteen-year-old.'

'Then let him get on with it, even if it means you having to make a fresh start somewhere else. That's what your father did, after all.' Steph's Italian father had been a violinist who had moved from the famed La Fenice orchestra in Venice to the Royal Philharmonic in London. He had married and settled happily over here, insisting on speaking to his daughter in Italian as much as possible so that she could learn the language. And it had worked. 'You could always look for something in Italy.'

'Let's not get carried away, Mum. I haven't dumped him yet.'

'But I think you will.' Her mother sounded as though she was in no doubt. 'Your happiness is the most important thing. There must be loads of other jobs in the music business.'

'We've been through this time and time again. There aren't as many as you'd think and certainly very few well-paid ones. At least with this job I can keep the wolf from the door, which is more than I was doing as a session musician.' With an awful lot of hard work and the unfailing support and encouragement of her parents she had managed to get to university, emerging with a music degree and a massive student-loan debt. After university she had spent several years trying to survive as a keyboard player but in the end she had bitten the bullet and looked for something more secure. The result had been her current job, working for Ethan. As time had gone by, she had found herself drawn closer and closer to him until they had moved in together.

Any further comment was interrupted by her phone. She picked it up and groaned inwardly as she checked the caller ID. For a moment or two she toyed with the idea of not answering but then decided she had no choice. He was her boss after all.

'Ethan, hi.' Out of the corner of her eye she saw her mother roll her eyes heavenwards. 'What's new?'

'How do you fancy a few weeks in Italy? By the seaside. You're half Italian, after all. You should love it.'

'Are you talking about taking a holiday?' Steph was genuinely amazed. This was a first. Ethan rarely took time off – unless it was to party into the small hours. As for herself, apart from regular trips to Venice with her parents to spend time with her dad's extended family, the only other time she had been abroad had been a cheap and not so cheerful trip with a former boyfriend to the Costa del Sol five years ago where a bathroom full of cockroaches and a twelve-hour delay at Malaga airport on the way back hadn't inspired any desire in her to travel anywhere since.

'I'm sure we'll have time to holiday as well, but this is a job, and a good one.' He was sounding remarkably bubbly.

'In Italy? Why go to Italy?'

'Because that's where the job is, and we're needed pronto.'

'But what about the studio here? We've got people booked in all the way through September.'

'They can wait.' He sounded dismissive and she was about to retort when he elaborated. 'But Royalty can't.'

'Royalty?' She knew she was sounding gormless, but she couldn't shake the image of Charles and Camilla that suddenly materialised in her head.

He was quick to explain. 'Royalty, the group. They want us to produce their new album.'

'Wow.' In spite of everything, Steph felt a surge of excitement run through her. Royalty really were royalty in the world of music. With platinum albums, BRIT and Grammy awards to their name, they had dominated the rock music scene throughout the nineties and well into the new century, even if they had dropped out of the limelight over the past few years. 'And they're reforming? I thought they'd split up.'

'They had and they are.' Ethan was sounding unusually animated. 'And they want me to produce their comeback album. Do you realise what this means?' In case she might be in any doubt, he spelt it out to her. 'This means the big time for me… for us. It doesn't get any bigger than this.'

'Wow.' Steph was aware that she was getting a bit repetitive but she had to agree. Being chosen to produce a brand-new album for a group whose fame ranked them up there alongside legends like Pink Floyd or Queen was huge. A thought occurred to her. 'But why Italy?'

'That's where Keith has his home nowadays, or at least one of his homes.'

'I see.' Keith Bailey was the leader of the group and he had achieved legendary status in the world of rock music, most notably for the famous millennium concert in Hyde Park in aid of world hunger. He had also hit the headlines, she remembered, for punching a renowned chat-show host live on air but that was a long time ago now. Hopefully he had mellowed with the passage of the years, otherwise this new contract might turn out to be fraught with problems. 'But what about a studio? We're going to need a truckful of gear, surely.'

'No need, he has his own. I've just come off the phone with him now. He's been telling me all about it. From what he's said, he's got even better gear than we have: some real traditional stuff and some state of the art.' He rattled off names and specifications of the recording equipment in Keith Bailey's Italian studio and Steph had to agree. This was top of the range stuff. Mind you, if anybody could afford that sort of thing, it was Royalty.

'Sounds good. When does he want us?'

'Starting next weekend.'

'Blimey, talk about short notice.' She thought frantically. The doctor had said she would arrange the mammogram this week so presumably that wouldn't be a problem, but there were other considerations as well. 'We're going to need to contact the performers we have booked in for the next month and put them off. They aren't going to be happy.'

'We'll offer them a fifty percent reduction in our rates to make up for it. That should keep them sweet.'

Steph glanced at her watch. 'We need to start calling people as soon as possible. I'm round at Mum's for tea. I could be back at the studio by seven thirty. Do you want me to come straightaway?'

'Enjoy your tea and then come back. It'll be fine.' He was sounding chirpier than she had heard him for ages. Maybe, she wondered, this would be the kick-start he needed to give up the Bad Boy lifestyle and concentrate on carving out his career for real – and he really was good at his job. Everybody said so and the fact that Royalty were coming to him proved it. And, she realised, if this did indeed signify him turning over a new leaf, maybe this new Ethan might also change back into the man she had fallen for three years ago.

Over the chocolate cake Steph told her mum all about it. Although her mum had little interest in modern music she knew the name Royalty, but Steph had to spell out how significant it was that she and Ethan were going to be involved in the group's first record in years. A quick search on her phone told her that it was almost exactly a decade since their last public appearance. 'As comebacks go, this is one of the greatest. Maybe not quite like reforming the Beatles but still huge.'

'Now I come to think of it, didn't you have a Royalty poster on your bedroom wall for years?'

Steph grinned at the memory. 'Yes, all the way through school I had the most enormous crush on Ben, the bass player. In fact, half of the girls in my class did.'

'And now you're going to meet the man in person.' Her mother grinned back at her. 'Maybe you'll end up dumping Ethan in favour of a rock star.'

Steph shook her head. 'I hardly think so. When I was a teenager, he was probably already in his thirties.' She did a quick bit of mental arithmetic. 'That probably makes him fifty now. I'm not sure how I'd feel about dating a man who's twenty years older than me.'

'A *multi-millionaire rock star* who's twenty years older than you.' There was a distinct twinkle in her mum's eye. 'You wouldn't be the first. Mind you...' Her mother hadn't forgotten what they had been talking about before Ethan's phone call. 'If you get Ethan to yourself for a bit, away from his toxic friends, it might mean that you and he...' She didn't need to say more.

'We'll see, Mum. Here's hoping it changes him back to the man he used to be.'

Chapter 2

The following Sunday she and Ethan flew to Pisa. All the way over on the plane Steph had tried to keep her mind on the job rather than on what the radiographer had said on Friday. After both a mammogram and an ultrasound scan, she had informed Steph that they would get the results to her in a week or so and told her to try not to worry. The very fact that she had told her not to worry had had the opposite effect and the possible outcomes had been uppermost in Steph's mind since then. Because she was coming over to Italy the clinician made a note to ensure that she would get the results by email, rather than letter, and indicated that they shouldn't take too long. As far as Steph was concerned, she just hoped the news whenever it came would be good.

Upon arrival in Italy, they took a train from the airport to the main station and picked up a train heading north. Keith Bailey's holiday home was less than an hour up the coast between Pisa and Genoa but Steph had been unable to locate it on Google Earth. Luckily somebody would be coming to pick them up at the nearby station when they got there.

The train journey was comfortable in their air-conditioned carriage, and the views, superb. To the left of the railway line was flat terrain with a series of long sandy beaches, surrounded by houses, hotels and restaurants.

Clearly this area was a major holiday destination. This was the first time Steph had been to the west coast of Italy and she was fascinated to see palm trees among huge umbrella pines on one side of the railway and snowy slopes on the mountains to the right of them. Considering it was the first of September and the temperature down here at the coast very high, she was amazed. It wasn't as if these were the High Alps, after all. However, a quick search on her phone revealed that what she could see wasn't snow after all but the white marble of the Apuan Alps cloaking the hillsides above places like Massa and Carrara. Apparently Carrara marble had been Michelangelo's material of choice for his sculptures and she wondered if she would have time to get across to Florence to see his masterpiece: the huge statue of David.

She suggested this to Ethan but received only a grunt in return. He hadn't come home the previous night until long after she had fallen asleep and she could still smell drink on his breath now. She had almost had to pour him into the cab this morning and had given him a serious talking-to as they waited for their flight, but he had been monosyllabic and uncommunicative all day. Her hopes that this exciting new job might prove to be the spark to snap him out of his spiral of self-indulgent excess were looking less and less likely to be realised. Maybe, she told herself, clutching at straws, when he found himself mixing with famous names like Royalty, a sea change would come over him.

But she wasn't holding her breath.

The train arrived at the little station at Sarzana bang on time and she was impressed by the punctuality. For somebody used to the vagaries of commuter trains in and out of London, this was refreshing. Stepping out of the cool interior on the other hand was anything but refreshing. A digital sign indicated that the afternoon temperature was thirty-three degrees and she could well believe it. Compared to the damp grey day she had left behind in England it was quite a shock to the system. She was just starting to tug her suitcase along the platform when a man approached and addressed himself to Ethan.

'Good afternoon, are you Ethan Carson? My name's Cesare. I look after Signor Bailey when he's here in Italy. Can I help you with your bags?'

The speaker was a friendly-looking man in his fifties with a luxuriant handlebar moustache that wouldn't have disgraced a pantomime villain. His English was fluent and he spoke with a lilting Italian accent which reminded Steph of her father and immediately endeared the man to her. Her dad had been a major influence on her life and she still missed him terribly.

Ethan roused himself from his stupor sufficiently to produce a response. 'Yeah, hi. Thanks. Here…'

It came as no surprise to Steph that Ethan omitted to introduce her or that he handed over his collection of bags to Cesare while leaving her to haul hers along unaided. For a second or two she caught the Italian's eye and shrugged. He gave her an encouraging look.

'Can I take your bag as well, signora?' Although it would have been a struggle with his hands already full.

She gave him a grateful smile and replied in Italian. 'That's okay, thanks. I can manage. My name's Stephanie. I'm the recording engineer.'

'I'm pleased to meet you, Stephanie, or should I say Stefania? My compliments on your Italian. You're very fluent. Are you English or Italian?'

She gave him a brief résumé of her family background as they walked out of the station and he offered his condolences for the loss of her father. He led them out into a small square in front of the station where the car was parked. Steph had been wondering what sort of flashy car a rock star might own and was almost disappointed to find they were to travel in an anonymous minibus. Of course, she reminded herself, Cesare was only the hired hand. No doubt Keith Bailey and his fellow band members would have their luxury cars at the house, wherever that was. According to what Ethan had been told, she and Ethan would be staying in the 'guest apartment' and she wondered what this would consist of. The way things had been going with Ethan, separate bedrooms would be a bonus.

After Cesare had lifted all the bags into the cavernous boot, they climbed into the van. Ethan subsided onto the back seat so Steph opted to sit up front alongside the driver. She let him negotiate his way out of town and onto a busy road heading towards a range of low tree-covered hills before engaging him in conversation.

'Is it far to Mr Bailey's house?'

He shook his head. 'Another fifteen minutes or so. It's just past Lerici.'

'I don't know this part of Italy.' She remembered seeing the name on the map. 'That's on the coast, isn't it?'

'Yes, indeed. Lerici's on the eastern side of the Gulf of Poets, the place where some of your greatest poets like Shelley and Byron came to stay and write. It's a beautiful area and Signor Bailey's house is just to the south of the town, right on the coast.'

At school Steph had studied the great Romantic poets of the first half of the nineteenth century but she couldn't

15

recall the name Lerici coming up. To be honest, she hadn't been terribly keen on poetry, but there was a first time for everything so maybe she would have to check out Shelley and Byron again. At that moment they crested a saddle between two taller hills and a stunning panorama opened up below them.

'Wow, that's amazing.' She gazed in awe at the almost unrealistically blue sea dotted with boats and a handful of islands. It was like something on a poster or a scene from a travel programme and it certainly couldn't have been more different from London. 'I can see why a poet would choose this place.' Returning her attention to Cesare she carried on. 'And what's Mr Bailey's house like? Is it very old?'

'The opposite. It's very modern. It was built only twenty years ago by a film director, but he got into financial difficulties and Signor Bailey bought it from him five, no, six, years ago. My wife and I've been running the place for him since then.'

'And I believe Ethan and I are staying in the guest apartment. Is that part of the house?'

'No, that's a much older building. It's what used to be a pair of fishermen's houses down by the beach. Signor Bailey converted the ground floor into a recording studio and turned the upper floor into guest accommodation. I'm sure you'll be very comfortable there.'

A minute or two later, they turned off the main road in the direction of Lerici. Cesare told her that the main road continued towards La Spezia, which was a major base for the Italian navy. When she asked him if it was worth a visit he shrugged his shoulders.

'If you like sailors. With its big boatyards it's pretty chaotic compared to the southern part of the gulf, although Portovenere on the other side of La Spezia's very pretty. No, Lerici's much nicer than La Spezia.'

As they descended towards the sea the landscape became increasingly built up and the streets of the little town when they got there were crowded with cars and holidaymakers. Steph gazed in anticipation at no fewer than four ice-cream shops – each with twenty or thirty different flavours and colours on display – enticing clothes shops and one delicatessen outside which they had to wait for almost a minute while an ambulance squeezed past. She barely recognised half of the items on display, hanging from hooks, spilling out of steel trays and filling glass jars like an old alchemist's wares. One thing was for sure: she was going to come back to Lerici for a visit.

Ten minutes of stop/start driving later they emerged from the houses again onto a tortuous and much narrower road that wound its way southwards around the rugged, steeply sloping hillside directly above the coast. As Lerici disappeared behind them they found themselves in an unspoilt area of rocky outcrops and dense woodland, interrupted every now and then by steep-sided ravines that offered tantalising glimpses of the deep cerulean blue of the sea below.

A minute or two later they reached a pair of sturdy metal gates set between stone gateposts with imposing wire fencing several metres high disappearing into the trees on either side of the gates. Cesare slowed and as he did so the gates began to open automatically. Steph couldn't miss the security cameras mounted on a steel pillar just inside. Clearly, Keith Bailey was taking no chances of being disturbed by unwanted visitors. Steph couldn't blame him. Being a world-renowned star presumably came with drawbacks, although the benefits probably far outweighed any such concerns.

Cesare drove in, and the gates were already closing behind them as they set off down a gently sloping narrow gravelled drive through the pine trees. This soon opened up into a broad, relatively flat area where four or five vehicles were parked. Steph didn't know much about cars, but the sleek silver convertible alongside which they parked absolutely screamed excess. A swift glance at the prancing horse emblem on the steering wheel as she climbed out into the heat of the sun confirmed her suspicions. She was in the land of the wealthy and privileged now – probably the over-privileged – and for the first time she wondered if she was going to like Keith Bailey and his entourage. She had met enough arrogant overpaid performers over the past few years to know that the prospect of spending up to a month among such people might not turn out to be a bed of roses.

As far as beds of a more practical nature were concerned, she was pleased to find that the guest apartment boasted no fewer than three bedrooms, all with huge beds and luxurious private bathrooms. Cesare walked them to their accommodation down a flight of stone steps between huge fragrant rosemary bushes covered in little blue flowers and alive with the buzzing of bees. Coming from London it really was like entering a different, enchanted world, and Steph loved every part of it. Entry to the old stone building was through a fine wooden door. This led into a hallway and Cesare pointed out the door to the studio on the right-hand side and a stairway straight in front leading up to the guest apartment. She climbed up and when she got there she found that it was every bit as swish as the Ferrari up the hill.

The views from the windows were spectacular and Steph stood and stared, spellbound. She could hardly believe that a two-hour flight could have transported her to somewhere so gorgeous. Although her Italian grandparents lived near Venice, which was unquestionably a wonderful historic city, the seaside around there that she had visited as a girl had been fairly flat and uninteresting. Here the scenery was much more spectacular. These old fishermen's houses had been built on the edge of low cliffs, probably only ten or twenty metres above a little cove, and from up here she could see deep into the crystal-clear water and, as she looked on, a shoal of little blue-and-grey fish flitted across the seabed. It was totally charming. She heard footsteps behind her and turned to see Cesare arriving at the top of the stairs with her suitcase, which he had insisted upon carrying up for her.

'Thank you so much, Cesare. That's ever so kind. I've just been admiring the view. I can see why Mr Bailey chose this place. It's fantastic.'

'I couldn't agree more. Every morning when I get up and look out I almost have to pinch myself to prove to myself that I'm not dreaming. Like your father, I'm from the north. I was born and brought up in the suburbs of Milan – not the nice luxurious ones – and then I served thirty years in the Italian navy, much of my time spent in a two metre by two metre steel cabin. Coming here six years ago has been a liberation. I love this place and I'm glad you feel the same way about it.'

He switched to English for the last sentence, glancing across to see if Ethan was similarly impressed by the view, but all he got was a vague nod of the head. Undeterred, he carried on in English and addressed himself to Ethan anyway.

'Signora Faye told me to tell you to take your time and settle in. When you feel like it, she invites you to come up to the villa for afternoon tea and to meet the family.' His face split into a grin. 'Tea's what you English people like, isn't it?'

Seeing as there was still no reaction from Ethan, Steph answered for both of them. 'That's very kind. Tell me, Cesare; Signora Faye, is she Mr Bailey's wife?'

He nodded. 'Yes, indeed, and she's a lovely person. I'm sure you'll like her.'

That sounded promising, but Steph wondered how they would get on with Keith Bailey himself. Certainly his reputation painted him as a mercurial character capable of acts of great kindness, but also of volcanic explosions of ill-temper. Hopefully the passage of the years and life in these gorgeous surroundings would have calmed him down, otherwise the next few weeks promised to be hard going.

She knew she needed to change out of her travelling clothes into something much lighter and, by the look of him, Ethan would probably benefit from a long cold shower to clear his head, so she glanced at her watch.

'It's three thirty now. Would it be all right if we come up to the villa at four?'

'Perfect. I'll tell Signora Faye.'

After he had left, Steph led Ethan into the first of the bedrooms and almost pushed him into the marble-clad bathroom. 'You need to take a shower and change before we go up to the villa. Get on with it.' She even turned on the water in the shower for him, resisting the temptation to turn the thermostat all the way to the blue extra cold setting, and left him to it.

Delaying a final decision on whether she felt like cohabiting with him, she used the next-door bathroom for her own shower. When she emerged and returned to the first room she was reassured to see Ethan buttoning himself into a clean shirt and jeans. His hair was still damp and he looked refreshed and she felt a little wave of relief. Slipping on a lightweight cotton dress she checked herself out in the mirror. She would do.

'Have we got time to take a look at the studio, Steph?' His voice also sounded more normal now.

She looked at her watch again before answering. 'It's five to four. If you're ready, I'm ready, so, yes, we've got time for a quick look before going up to the villa.'

The studio was accessed through the door they had seen in the entrance lobby on the ground floor and a cursory glance confirmed what Ethan had been told on the phone. It was immaculate; an eclectic mix of vintage and ultra-modern equipment, but all of it unmistakably top of the range. She felt rising excitement and looked across at Ethan's face, which reflected her own. He looked like the proverbial kid in a candy store as he ran his hands reverently over the console, microphones, speakers and other gear. When he returned his attention to her, she was delighted to see him looking and sounding more like a serious music producer once more.

'This is the stuff of dreams. If we can't produce a great album here, we don't deserve to be in the business.'

'Well, of course, the band members probably will have to have some hand in it...'

'Band members? They don't produce the goods, we do. I've told you before and I'll tell you again: I can turn a voice like a chainsaw into a thing of beauty if I need to. And with gear like this I've got all I need.'

Steph had always admired his self-confidence, which had proved time and time again to be well justified, but she thought she had better add a word of caution. 'Well, just remember who you're dealing with here. Royalty aren't just any old band, so you treat them with respect. Right? You're good at your job but so are they… or at least, they were.'

They climbed the stone steps to the car parking area and from there up yet more steps, this time flanked by a subtropical display of huge prickly cactus, date palms, banana plants and a host of succulents dispersed amid the rocky outcrops that thrust through the bone-dry soil. Lizards scrambled for cover as they passed by and a pair of brilliant blue dragonflies flitted along ahead of them. The steps led to a long sun terrace from where they had a panoramic view of the gulf. The villa itself was stunning and Steph paused to admire it, still barely able to believe that she had been transported into such luxury. It was so different from the flat where they lived in London that she felt like an alien, and she knew there was no way she could ever fit into a lifestyle like this. This only added to the feeling of apprehension that had been building inside her all day.

The villa was a long white building with a flat roof, and the front wall was a near unbroken expanse of glass. An arched veranda ran the length of the house providing shade and at the far end there was a swimming pool. Beside this, under a pergola covered in vines, was a group of people. Among them, instantly recognisable, was Keith Bailey. As he saw them, he leapt to his feet and came over to shake hands, first with Ethan and then with her. To Steph's relief, there was a smile on his face and he looked welcoming.

'Ethan, my man, it's good to see you again. The last time I saw you, you were still working for that crook, Delbert. I'm glad you've gone out on your own since then.'

Steph remembered that Keith was quite a bit older than the other band members and he had always been the leader of the group on and off stage. Despite now being close to sixty, he appeared to have aged gracefully. His hair was still the same jet-black colour – suspiciously black – although now cut a lot shorter than before, just grazing his collar at the back. The diamonds in his earrings sparkled in the sunlight and he was smartly dressed in a polo shirt, white shorts and the regulation rock star dark glasses, although in fairness they might have been for the sun. He could have just stepped off the golf course; apart, maybe, from the earrings.

Steph was pleased to see Ethan looking and sounding polite and professional as he replied. 'Hi, Keith. Leaving Delbert was the best thing I've ever done, and it's great to see you, too.' He then surprised Steph by introducing her without being prompted. 'And this is my right-hand woman, Steph Zanin, who's a wizard on the console. Steph, this guy doesn't need any introduction, right?'

'I'm very pleased to meet you, Mr Bailey.' Steph shook hands with the great man and was rewarded with a welcoming smile.

'Hi, Steph, and do call me Keith. Only police officers and judges call me Mr Bailey – or at least they used to. Come and let me introduce you to the rest of the gang. Faye, come say hi to our new arrivals.'

Steph gave a surreptitious sigh of relief. So far so good. No sign of the irascible Keith Bailey; at least not yet.

Faye, Keith's wife, was a very attractive and stylish woman with remarkably blonde, almost silver hair. She was wearing a beautiful purple wrap over her swimming costume and as she stood up to shake hands and chat, Steph was impressed at how youthful she looked. From what she remembered reading, Faye had to be well into her fifties, but she had the skin of a twenty-year-old. Her age was confirmed in conversation a moment later when she told them that she and Keith would be celebrating their thirtieth wedding anniversary at the end of the week. She and her husband appeared relaxed and comfortable together as a couple, which was good to see. Steph congratulated them and was genuinely happy for her, secretly marvelling that a rock 'n' roll marriage had lasted so successfully when so many tended to end up in tatters, not least when one of the partners in this marriage had a reputation as a tearaway.

Keith patted Steph's arm and pointed to another man. 'And I daresay you recognise this guy.'

The tall man wearing a white cheesecloth shirt, blue shorts and matching blue tinted sunglasses was the group's drummer, Johnny Carter. She knew him to be in his fifties as well, but he was also still recognisably the same guy, with a mane of hair tied in a ponytail, although there were now a few hints of grey at his temples and his face was a bit more lined and creased. Alongside him was a mumsy-looking lady who was introduced as his wife, Tara. Steph took an immediate liking to her and they chatted for several minutes while Ethan and the two band members talked shop. Steph would dearly have liked to join in the technical discussion, but she bided her time for now.

Then Tara gave Steph a real shock. 'Have you met Ben?'

Steph followed the direction of her eyes and spotted two figures lying on sunbeds further along under the shade of the vines. One was a red-haired woman and beside her was a man. Steph had to make a conscious effort not to look aghast as she realised that this was her teenage crush, Ben Smiley, the bass player and the baby of the group. Like the others, he had disappeared from circulation for almost a decade, but unlike the others, he hadn't been looking after himself. She was confronted by the vision of a dishevelled man with an unruly mass of grey hair, wearing sweatpants and a faded Bruce Springsteen T-shirt. She knew him still to be barely fifty, but he looked sixty or even older. She had a hard job keeping the shock off her face as she went over to shake hands with him.

'I'm delighted to meet you. I'm Steph. I'm the recording engineer.'

He didn't stand up and just gave her a lazy wave of the hand. He looked zonked, although there might have been a hint of a smile beneath the dark glasses on his weary face.

'Hi, Steph. Good to see you. You met my wife?'

'Hi, Steph. I'm Lottie. Welcome to paradise.'

Steph turned and shook hands with the redhead whose friendly smile came as another pleasant surprise. Somehow Steph had been expecting these super-rich people to be far more stand-offish, but such was evidently not the case. 'Hi, Lottie. Yes, it's an amazing place, isn't it? Do you come here every summer?'

'I wish…' Lottie gave a little sigh. 'We only arrived yesterday, and this is just about the first holiday Ben and I've had for years.' She waved vaguely towards the pool and the sea beyond. 'It beats the hell out of Hampshire.'

'Is that where you live?'

'Halfway between Andover and Winchester. It's a lovely spot but we don't very often get this sort of weather. Ah, here's Donatella with the tea. She's the most amazing cook. Just you wait.'

Steph looked back along the terrace to see a lady with greying hair emerge from the massive gaping tri-fold doors pushing a tea trolley. On it were two teapots, jugs of hot water and milk and what looked like scones. Apart from the scenery, they could have been in a traditional English tea house. All that was lacking was a big dollop of clotted cream, but Steph knew that that wasn't an Italian thing. The whole experience was so unexpected, not least as Steph's limited experience of rock star parties definitely involved far more sinister substances than tea and scones, but there was no sign of anything hallucinogenic on the trolley. It was certainly looking as if the band members of Royalty had moved on from a life of sex, drugs and rock 'n' roll, although Ben's lethargic state was concerning. Hopefully Ethan would follow their example and clean up his act. But she wasn't counting on it.

After a cup of tea and an excellent freshly baked scone with what was almost certainly homemade strawberry jam, Steph watched as Keith and Ethan disappeared inside the house, presumably to discuss plans for the forthcoming days. Keith didn't invite her to join them and Ethan didn't even glance over at her, so she bit her tongue and decided to go for a walk to clear her head. Obviously his 'right-hand woman' wasn't important enough to be included in the conversation. Suppressing a few choice words, she thanked Faye and the others and went back down the steps past the studio and continued along a path that curled down the steep hillside to the little beach.

The beach itself was barely the size of a tennis court, covered in glorious golden sand. Slipping off her sandals she headed for the water and immediately discovered that the sand was scalding hot underfoot. She hopped hastily over to the waterline and let the Mediterranean cool her feet and her temper. Ethan was the boss and it was up to him to decide whether she should be included in any negotiations. Her job would start once the group came down to the studio so until then she resolved to concentrate on enjoying this place that Lottie had described as paradise; and not without justification.

On either side of the beach jagged rocky headlands protected the bay from the open sea and there was barely a ripple on the water in here. The only sign of human activity was at the end of the southern headland where the red roof of a house was just visible. From the faded look of the old roof tiles, this was quite probably another ancient fisherman's cottage. Certainly, a fisherman couldn't really ask to be much closer to the sea. The water was so clear that Steph could see down to the seabed for a long way, and so she stood there, mesmerised, staring down into it. The seabed was mostly sand with occasional weed-covered rocks. She didn't spot any more fish, but she suddenly discovered another, bigger animal out there, swimming towards the beach. From the wet shiny black head and the nose just sticking above the surface her first reaction was that she was looking at a seal. As the animal approached, however, she realised that it was in fact a dog, a big dog, and it was heading straight towards her.

Steph didn't have much experience of dogs. Her parents had worked full time so they had never had one in the house and her mother had made sure she kept her clear of any they met while out and about when Steph was little. As a result, Steph viewed the approach of what was clearly a big dog with some trepidation. This was quickly revealed to be unnecessary – well, sort of. Emerging from the sea, the big black animal trotted towards her, its tail wagging in a friendly fashion. It certainly didn't look in the least bit aggressive and she allowed herself to begin to relax.

The trouble was that as she hesitantly held out her hand for the dog to sniff – knuckles first as she had been taught – it had barely touched her hand with its nose before it decided to shake itself vigorously. In a matter of seconds, she found herself on the receiving end of a shower of canine-scented water that soaked her and reduced her brand-new frock to a soggy mess.

'Oh, dog, did you have to?'

Apparently pleased to be addressed by her, irrespective of her choice of language, the dog came closer and leant its soaking wet body against her leg, looking up at her with two big brown eyes, tail wagging lazily. She couldn't stay annoyed with it for long, so she crouched down and stroked the big hairy head as she checked the animal out. She knew enough about dogs to recognise that this was a black Labrador, and she knew enough about anatomy to recognise that he was a male dog. He possessed a fine set of gleaming white teeth and a long pink tongue which appeared intent on licking every inch of her hands. He was wearing a red collar and attached to it was a little steel disc with a phone number on it; no name. She looked around to see where his master or mistress might be but saw no sign of anybody. Maybe he belonged up at the house. She was still wondering if she should go back and tell somebody she had found a dog when there was a whistle from somewhere above her and the dog was off like a shot. Presumably the Labrador was returning to his master.

The dog didn't take the same track that had led her down here but ran to the other end of the beach and disappeared up a narrower path through the scrub. For a moment she thought she glimpsed the figure of a man up there among the broom bushes, but he disappeared from sight almost immediately. She was glad the man hadn't come down to the beach as a glance at her soaking wet dress plastered against her body decided her in favour of a hasty return to the guest apartment for another shower and a change of clothes.

Chapter 3

Ethan had told her to bring some 'smart' clothes as well as her usual stuff and, although she knew there was no way she would be able to compete with the outfits of the rock 'n' roll elite, she had gone shopping a few days earlier and bought two new dresses, not garments she wore very often. Unfortunately, one was currently soaking in the basin to remove the lingering Labrador odour and depending on how it dried out and whether she could borrow an iron, she knew she might have to look for a replacement. She was cheered by the thought that this did, of course, provide her with a solid reason for making that visit to Lerici and its ice-cream parlours. This only left her with the other dress, a rather nice light blue one that fitted her well. As ever, Ethan didn't appear to notice and certainly didn't comment, but she was used to that by now.

She and Ethan went back up to the villa at seven and found the group inside the huge lounge, with air conditioning providing welcome relief from the heat. There was aircon in the guest apartment as well but she hadn't turned it on, preferring to open the windows as wide as they would go. Walking into the lounge, she heard the sound of music and realised that it was coming from Keith.

He was sitting on a leather armchair with an acoustic guitar rather than his trademark electric guitar on his knees. He wasn't playing one of Royalty's songs. In fact it wasn't rock music at all. Instead, he was quietly strumming a gentle melody that she didn't recognise and it sounded good. Cesare was standing behind a fully fitted bar on one side of the room, nodding his head in time to the music and just along from him Johnny had joined in. Instead of a drum kit, in front of him on the bar were three glasses, each containing different quantities of water, and he was beating time against the glasses with a pair of plastic cocktail sticks and occasionally thumping his palms on the bar.

Faye Bailey was sitting across the room from them on a sofa along with Johnny's wife, Tara, and she beckoned to Steph to join her while Ethan headed for the bar.

'Come and sit down, Steph. That's a lovely dress.'

Faye gave her an appreciative look and Steph checked her out in return. She had changed out of her swim-suit but she wasn't wearing anything outrageous; just a very smart linen blouse and a cotton skirt. Considering she had been part of the rock 'n' roll scene for decades, Steph had been expecting something more ostentatious. Beside her, Tara could have been any suburban housewife in her flowery frock, although Steph could recall photos of her back in the nineties when she had scandalised the press with her outfits and behaviour. The tabloids had even nicknamed her Tara the Otter after she and Johnny had been caught skinny-dipping in the Serpentine.

Steph gave them both a little smile as she sat down. 'Thanks a lot. I feel so privileged to hear two megastars giving a personal recital. Is this something they do regularly?'

Faye shook her head. 'They haven't played together since Vince died.' Steph remembered hearing the news of the death of the group's keyboard player while she was still at university: a fall from a seventh storey window as a result of a drug overdose. 'In fact, this is just about the first time all three have been in the same room together since Vince's funeral.' As she spoke, the lounge door opened and Steph was pleased to see Ben appear, looking remarkably bright considering that barely an hour earlier he had looked so weary. Like Johnny, his hair was now pulled back in a ponytail but, unlike the drummer, his was silver grey all over. As Keith spotted him Steph couldn't miss the welcoming smile that spread across his face.

'Ben, great, come over here and jam with us.'

Alongside Ben was his wife, Lottie, and Steph saw her give her husband a gentle push towards the other two men. When she was sure he was on his way, Lottie came across to where Tara and Faye were sitting with Steph and addressed them in little more than a nervous whisper. 'I wonder if he'll want to join in.'

Tara added in equally hushed tones, 'Did he bring a guitar?'

'He didn't but I did.' Lottie gave them a conspiratorial grin. 'I managed to stick his favourite one in, but he doesn't know. We had so many bags he never noticed.'

Steph listened with some perplexity, dying to ask why they were talking in whispers, but she decided it wasn't her place to intrude in their conversation. She looked on as Ben perched on a bar stool, but he made no attempt even to speak to the other two men. Cesare came over to him, but Ben just shook his head and waved him away. Clearly, he wasn't craving alcohol, which also came as a bit of a surprise considering his reputation for wild living back in the day.

The other two stopped playing and there was a pregnant pause that lasted for several minutes before Keith looked back down at his guitar and started playing the unmistakable intro to the Rolling Stones' classic 'I Can't Get No Satisfaction'. Johnny joined in on percussion and by the time the song finished, the glasses on the bar looked in danger of being knocked off by his impromptu drumsticks. Ben, however, made no move to take part and just sat there looking impassive. As they came to the end, Keith looked across straight at him.

'Remember when we first played that, Ben?'

After a momentary hesitation Ben replied. 'Yeah, I remember.'

Although these were barely three words, looks of considerable satisfaction appeared on Keith and Johnny's faces. 'We could never forget that, could we?' Keith looked over towards where Steph was sitting with Faye, Tara and Lottie. 'That was the opening number of our very first gig. Some scruffy old pub in Gravesend – I forget the name. At that time, we weren't writing our own stuff and were just doing covers of all the famous bands.' He glanced back at Ben. 'How about this one?'

And he launched into the opening to David Bowie's 'Space Oddity'. Steph knew and loved Bowie's songs and she found herself nodding along to the tune. Once again Ben played no part in it but the three words he had uttered appeared to have somehow lightened the atmosphere in the room. Steph looked forward to finding out more about the subplot; just what was the relationship between the three remaining band members nowadays?

Cesare came across to ask what they wanted to drink. Lottie opted for a Coke while Faye persuaded Steph and Tara to join her in a glass of 'fizz'. When this arrived, it turned out to be a bottle of Bollinger and Steph was almost reassured to see that here at least was a hint of the sort of rock-star excess she had been expecting, as compared to the garden party atmosphere that afternoon. She had limited experience of champagne but a sip from her glass – she was determined to stay sober and hoped Ethan would do the same – confirmed that it was very good.

A couple of minutes later a blonde woman in her thirties came into the room accompanied by a man wearing a vivid green Hawaiian shirt, skinny jeans with strategic tears around the knees and flip flops on his feet. His head was completely shaved, and he had a close-cropped jet-black beard that finished abruptly level with his ears. One thing was for sure: Steph knew she would have no trouble picking him out in an identity parade. Faye waved them over and introduced them to Steph.

'Steph, this is our daughter, Sky, and her fiancé, Tom. Sky, Steph's here with Ethan to teach Dad how to work the recording studio.'

As Steph shook hands she reflected on Faye's choice of words. Why hadn't she mentioned the new album? Strange.

'Hi, Steph.' Sky shared her mother's friendly smile and the resemblance between mother and daughter was striking. 'It's always great to meet an expert.'

'I'm just the recording engineer. Ethan does all the important stuff.' Even if this was increasingly not the case. 'Have you and Tom been here for the whole summer?'

'Most of August, but we're leaving any day now. Tom needs to get back to Manchester to work and so do I.' She lowered her voice and glanced over to the door. 'Besides, we need to get away.'

Steph followed the direction of her eyes and saw the door open. In came a man she recognised as Keith's son, Denver, a singer in his own right, although according to Ethan, not in his father's league. He was a tall, good-looking man who exuded confidence. Draped against him was an attractive woman at least ten years his junior whose skin-tight top left little to the imagination. Her hair was dyed blonde, although the dark roots were showing, and her inch-long fingernails had been adorned with the Stars and Stripes. She, too, would stand out in an ID parade.

As Denver's eyes landed on Steph his lips parted in a smile – the sort of smile a hungry lion gives a wounded antelope before tearing it into pieces and feasting on it – and she felt her skin creep. Nevertheless, remembering she was a guest in the house of VIPs, she managed to summon a smile as the couple approached.

'Hello, I'm Steph. I'm the recording engineer. It's good to meet you.' Although she had a feeling it wasn't going to be.

Denver Bailey extended an immaculately manicured hand and held onto Steph's for a couple of seconds longer than necessary. 'Delighted to meet you, Steph.' He didn't introduce the woman beside him, and he didn't introduce himself; no doubt assuming that he needed no introduction. 'I look forward to getting to know you better.' From the leer on his face it was pretty clear what he had in mind and one glance at the face of his flashy companion made it clear that she, too, knew what he meant. Steph found herself blinking apprehensively for fear that she might find those lethal-looking fingernails lunging for her eyes. No doubt sensing the tension in the air, Faye stepped in.

'Did you have a good day?'

Denver grimaced. 'Driving around in a Fiat? I can't see why the old man couldn't let me take the Ferrari.' In spite of being well into his thirties, he sounded like a spoilt child.

Faye shook her head. 'You know that's his pride and joy. He's the only one who gets to drive it. He doesn't even let me near the thing, not that I'd want to. It's far too wide and it's so damn low you can't see where you're going.'

Denver looked unconvinced and stood there irresolutely for a few moments. Steph wondered whether the couple were going to join their group but after an exchange of frosty glances with his sister, he led his girl-friend over to a neighbouring pair of armchairs. Putting two and two together wasn't difficult: Steph realised that relations between Denver and Sky were strained for whatever reason. However, instead of sitting down he shook the blonde off his arm as if she were an unwanted appendage and went over to where his father was strumming his guitar. The girl shot him a dark look and pouted like a miffed teenager as she sat down on her own. Somehow Steph got the feeling these two were made for each other.

Denver stood alongside his father until the end of the number before addressing him. 'Hi, Pop, you taking requests?'

For a fraction of a second an expression of reluctance flitted across both his father's face and Johnny's but disappeared again almost immediately. Ben at the bar remained impassive while Ethan looked more interested in his generous glass of gin and tonic as Keith replied.

'Yes, of course, Den. What do you want us to play?'

'Something I know the words to. Maybe something other than old Royalty numbers.' He wasn't exactly sneering, but there was a supercilious look on his face.

For a second or two it looked as though Keith was going to retort before Faye weighed in from across the room. Steph had a feeling this wasn't the first time she had been called on to act as buffer between father and son. 'Keith, you know I love the old stuff, even if Denver doesn't. Why don't you play one of the early Royalty ones? I know, play "Searching for Treasure". It's always been one of my favourites.'

Steph sat back and listened with considerable pleasure as Keith and Johnny reproduced an acoustic version of one of the group's most popular hits. She had listened to this over and over again as a teenager and knew every single word by heart, finding herself murmuring the lyrics under her breath as Keith sang them softly. He might have aged but his voice was still as sweet as ever and that boded well for the success of the new album. What very soon emerged was that Denver either didn't share her familiarity with the song or he was deliberately being obtuse as he did little more than nod along to it for a few bars before raising his hand and clicking his fingers imperiously in the direction of Cesare, mouthing the word 'Champagne', and returning to his girlfriend who was still looking miffed.

Dinner was served outside on the terrace overlooking the sea. The temperature was gradually dropping to a comfortable level as the sun set and there wasn't a breath of wind to stir the candles that illuminated the table. Steph loved Italian food and wondered what they were going to be served: Italian or English. After the very English afternoon tea, maybe they were going to get roast beef and Yorkshire pudding. She queried it with Faye who was sitting next to her.

'Definitely Italian. Donatella's an absolute treasure. Keith and I've always had a soft spot for Italy – we got married in Rome – but when we bought this place we never imagined we'd be able to find a cook of her calibre.'

'Do she and Cesare live here in the villa all year round?'

'That's right. That way we know there's somebody to keep an eye on the place. You've probably noticed all the steel gates and fences around here. We've never been burgled so far, thank God, but we feel so much better knowing that Cesare and Donatella are here. We don't live here full time, you see.'

'Where's home, if you don't mind me asking?'

'We have a house in Oxfordshire where we spend most of the year and we started off just coming here for a few weeks in summer. But we love this place so much we've been staying longer and longer. This year we've been here for almost three months and we're planning on staying for the whole of September.'

Steph had been concerned at how much work Cesare and his wife had to do to look after a dozen people but since the trade-off was two thirds of the year with this idyllic place to themselves, it seemed like a more than fair deal on both sides. No doubt there would still be jobs to be done in winter in the house and grounds but even so… Nice work if you can find it.

The antipasti arrived and Faye talked her through the selection of dishes on offer. 'As we're by the sea we eat a lot of fish but if that's a problem for you or Ethan, just say so. Donatella's got loads of other stuff.'

'I love fish and any kind of seafood.' Steph had never seen Ethan eat any fish apart from battered cod and chips but a glance across the table showed him already on his second glass of the excellent chilled white wine so she decided if he didn't like the food, he could lump it. He hadn't uttered a single word to her since coming up to the villa and she had already decided that for tonight at least she intended to sleep in one of the other bedrooms.

The antipasti consisted of cold seafood salad: a mixture of octopus, squid, prawns, mussels and other shellfish. In another big bowl was a mixed salad with quails' eggs, artichoke hearts and olives and yet another dish arrived containing filleted fish, freshly grilled and sprinkled with garlic and parsley. While Steph was still making up her mind, Faye reached over and spooned a couple of the little fish onto Steph's plate. 'I suggest you try these first while they're still warm.'

They were delicious. Accompanied by warm focaccia bread, the antipasti were a great success. In particular the seafood salad was exquisite and the pieces of octopus, once Steph had summoned up the courage to try the tentacles with their little suckers, were a real delicacy. She would dearly have liked to take a photo to send to her mum, but she restrained herself until she knew her hosts better. She washed it all down with a big mouthful of ice-cold sparkling mineral water and a smaller mouthful of equally cold white wine. This also tasted excellent, and she got the impression that Ethan shared her view as he continued to drain glass after glass.

Apart from him, however, the only other people around the table hitting the booze heavily appeared to be Denver and his girlfriend who were already on a second bottle of Bollinger. Sky's fiancé, Tom, chose a can of beer while Keith and Johnny drank wine but certainly not to excess. Ben and his wife drank no alcohol at all and Steph wondered if this was just tonight or whether they were teetotal. Certainly abstinence didn't tally with the stories of crazy drunken escapades she remembered reading about in years gone by.

The antipasti were followed by *fusilli ai frutti di mare*; curly pasta covered in a succulent seafood sauce containing clams and mussels. Steph cleared her plate with enjoyment, forgetting that according to Italian tradition, there was yet another course to come. Seeing the apprehension on Steph's face when Cesare gave her the news that there was more on the way, Sky gave her a grin.

'Don't worry. You don't have to eat it all. I think Donatella said she was going to do her signature stuffed squid so just have a taste if you're feeling full. I guarantee it's worth making a bit of space for.'

Sky was right. The stuffed squid arrived in a steaming dish straight from the oven and they looked like little white parcels no bigger than apples. Steph helped herself to the smallest one on the plate and inside she found chopped-up squid meat, breadcrumbs, parsley and garlic. The taste was exquisite, and as she ate she reflected that it was just as well she had no intention of kissing anybody tonight. Certainly, any self-respecting vampire would be keeping its distance after all the lovely garlic. And as far as she was concerned Ethan, who was still knocking back the wine like there was no tomorrow, could join the vampires well away from her room.

Chapter 4

When the morning came, Steph opened her eyes and lay in bed reflecting that she was glad she wasn't in Ethan's shoes. With everything he had drunk last night, she had a feeling all would not be too well inside his head when he eventually surfaced. After dinner, she had steered him back to the guest apartment, mildly surprised that he managed it without falling down the stone steps. Leaving him swaying by the bed in the first bedroom, she had removed herself and her bag to the room next door and she had a feeling he probably hadn't even noticed.

She reached for her watch and, seeing that it was still early, decided to go down to the beach for a paddle or even a swim. The dress the dog had soaked was on a hanger by the open window and a quick check revealed that it was now bone dry and no longer smelt of Labrador, but it was decidedly crumpled. She resolved to check in the cupboards to see if she could find an iron. If not, she could always ask Cesare.

She pulled on shorts and a T-shirt over her bikini, picked up a towel in case she did decide to go into the water and went down the stairs and out into the fresh air. It was cooler at this time of the morning but certainly not cold by a long chalk. The scent of rosemary, lavender and pine needles was in the air, and she breathed deeply as she made her way down the path to the beach, feeling it clean her lungs. The sand was still cool underfoot at this hour and she wandered along the waterline, scanning for shells just like she used to do on holiday with her parents when her dad was still alive. The thought of her dad reminded her that she might get the results of her scan later this week and she offered up a silent prayer that it would be good news. She did her best to concentrate on some beautiful little blue butterfly-wing-shaped shells and when she came to a stunning piece of glossy mother of pearl, she picked it up and slipped it into her shorts pocket as a souvenir of this lovely place.

She took two steps into the water and stood there with it lapping at her calves as she reflected on last night. Doing her best to ignore the fact that her boyfriend had yet again ended up drinking far too much – even if, to be fair, she hadn't seen him do anything to disgrace himself – she really couldn't have asked for a better welcome. Considering that she and Ethan were just the hired hands, she had been welcomed into the family as if she were a long-lost friend. Faye and Sky had been kind and hospitable and apart from Denver's ogling and his girlfriend's jealous stares, everybody had been most pleasant. In particular, Keith, despite his reputation for being hot tempered, had been relaxed and friendly.

The big unknown was just what the situation was as far as the new album was concerned. Nobody had yet mentioned it, at least not to her, and Ben had pointedly refused to join the other two in their improvised jam session. Could it be that he didn't yet know what Keith had in mind? Or had he already decided not to participate in reforming the band after a decade of silence? But, if so, what was he doing here? Not only had they not played together for ten years but, from what Faye had said, they hadn't even sat down together in all this time. Had they had a major falling-out? If so, what about? Alternatively, was there some other reason why Ben was keeping out of it while Keith was patently walking on eggshells around him? No doubt all would be revealed before too long.

Shrugging her shoulders, she turned and went back up the beach to a convenient rock and removed her T-shirt and shorts, setting them down on the flat top of the rock along with her towel and sandals. Making her way back across the sand she waded slowly out into the refreshingly cool, but far from cold, sea until she could sink down so that the water came up to her shoulders, before pushing herself forward and setting off in a slow breaststroke. She was a good swimmer and she carried on out to the mouth of the bay from where she had a fine view across to Lerici and La Spezia to the right, although a bigger headland prevented her from seeing far in the opposite direction. When she had time, she decided she would walk around the coast a bit to see what lay to the south of them.

A few minutes after returning to the beach, she was standing by her clothes, bending over as she finished drying her legs, when something cold and wet gave her an intimate prod in the posterior. She turned to see her friend the Labrador, tail wagging, evidently delighted to see her.

'*Ciao, bello*. And how are you today?'

In reply to this multilingual greeting, he just wagged his tail harder before turning and trotting off, to return almost immediately with a lump of driftwood in his mouth. He dropped it at her feet and turned so his nose was pointing at the sea. He couldn't have made himself any plainer if he had just asked her to pick it up and throw it. She did as requested, and he splashed joyfully into the water and swam out to retrieve it, immediately swimming back to the beach and dropping it at her feet again. She repeated the process several times until that same whistle she had heard the previous day echoed across the cove and the dog abandoned the game and started swimming to the shore. Back on dry land, he charged off up the little track and just for a moment or two Steph once again glimpsed a tall figure standing up there on the headland before he and the dog disappeared over the crest of the rise.

Breakfast was served on the terrace, and it came as no surprise to Steph to see Ethan's bedroom door still closed as she went out. She left him to it and went up to the villa at eight thirty. Sitting at the table were Faye and Keith along with Johnny's wife, Tara. Faye waved Steph into a seat opposite them just as Cesare emerged from the house with a basket of warm croissants.

'What can I get you, signora: bacon and egg, cereal or something else to eat? And what about to drink – a nice cappuccino maybe?' He addressed her in Italian, and she answered in the same language.

'Just a cappuccino please, and I'll try one of these croissants – and please call me Steph or Stefania.' She remembered what she wanted to ask. 'By the way, my dress got soaked when a big dog shook himself all over me down at the beach yesterday. I've rinsed it out and it's perfectly dry, but I was wondering if I could borrow an iron?'

'Just let me have it and Donatella will iron it for you.'

'I wouldn't dream of it. She's got more than enough to do. Seriously, just lend me an iron and I'll do it.'

He had another try but she remained adamant, so he went off to get her the iron. As he disappeared into the house, Faye smiled across the table at her. 'Wow, you speak

44

fantastic Italian. I just about got that you don't want bacon and eggs but what was the rest about? *Ferro*, wasn't it?'

Steph thanked her for the compliment and then went on to explain about the wet dog and her request for an iron.

When Keith heard about the Labrador, he gave an exasperated sigh. 'Rob's got to do something about Waldorf. I know he's still a youngster, but he can't go round soaking our guests.'

Steph wondered who Rob was but didn't want to sound nosey, so she started with the dog. 'You know the Labrador then? Waldorf – cool name. But there's no trouble; he's a super dog. In fact, he and I had a game of fetch this morning. Who does he belong to?'

Faye provided the answer. 'To our son, Robert. He lives out on the headland and has done for some years now. He speaks great Italian now, but Keith and I are still very much at an elementary level. We keep saying we'll take lessons, but with Rob and Cesare to do all the translating for us we've been too lazy. But you sound as if you really are Italian. How come?'

Steph relegated the question of why this son hadn't joined them last night until another time and told Faye about her family background. As she spoke, she found herself wondering about this family. She had already got the feeling that things weren't completely peachy between the two siblings she had already met, so maybe this other son's absence was because he was at daggers drawn with another member of the family. From what she had seen so far, the most likely candidate for this honour was Denver, but of course it could be Keith if the stories about him being quick-tempered were true. Whoever it was, Steph knew that it was no business of hers, so she stayed off the subject and just asked Faye about Robert's place of residence.

'When you say Robert lives in the house on the headland, do you mean full time?'

'That's right. He's been living there for four years now, and he loves Italy even more than we do. Every time I see him, he gets more and more Italian. He's ever so fluent now. To my untrained ear, he sounds just about as fluent as you do.'

'And is he musical too?'

'Very much so. He plays the violin. He performs all over Europe.'

Steph couldn't help an expression of surprise. 'The violin? Not really the instrument I would have expected the son of rock legend, Keith Bailey, to play.'

She was pleased to see Keith grin back at her over his cornflakes. 'It took me a while to get my head round it too but, boy, is he good! Even allowing for parental pride, he's a star.'

'Who's a star?' The voice belonged to Denver who appeared from the house and the mood of the table took a nosedive. 'You talking about me, Pop?'

Keith buried his face in his coffee cup and left it to his wife to reply. 'You're a star as well, but we were just talking about your brother and his dog.'

'That mutt!' It wasn't immediately clear whether Denver was referring to his brother or his pet. Still, it was such a beautiful morning that even grumpy Denver couldn't stay grumpy too long. He pulled out a chair and sat down alongside Steph. 'Hi, Steph. You're looking lovely today. Where's your boyfriend?'

It was on the tip of her tongue to tell him that Ethan was at risk of no longer occupying that position but she

46

still hadn't made that decision. She also realised that this might give Denver ideas, if he thought she was available, so she just smiled sweetly. 'He was very tired last night. He's still sleeping.'

'Sleeping it off.' Denver didn't mince his words. 'I haven't seen a man drink so much in one sitting since before my father took the pledge.' Before anybody could retort, he returned his attention to Steph. 'So if he's sleeping it off, does that mean you're free to come swimming with me? I'm sure you look good in a bikini.'

She managed to maintain the smile, but it was beginning to hurt by now. 'I've already had my swim this morning with Waldorf the dog, and I plan to spend the morning familiarising myself with all that lovely recording gear your father's got down in the studio.'

At that moment Denver's girlfriend appeared. From the icy expression on her face Steph had a feeling she had been listening for a while before emerging from the house. Ignoring Steph completely, she greeted Faye, Keith and Tara before taking a seat on the other side of Denver so close to him you couldn't have got a playing card between them.

'Good morning, Willow.' Faye produced a little smile for the girl's benefit. Today she looked barely of legal age. 'I like your top.'

Steph studiously avoided looking at her but had already been struck by the minuscule crop top that revealed a huge tattoo of what looked like an eagle splayed across the woman's stomach. Willow acknowledged the compliment with a nod.

'It's so hot. I thought September would be cool but it's boiling here, and Den wants to go to Florence today.

We'll probably get sunstroke.' Her American accent was more noticeable this morning.

Steph reflected that an effective way to avoid that eventuality would be for her to cover up a bit, but she left it unsaid. The good news as far as the rest of them were concerned was that Denver and Willow wouldn't be around today, which should reduce the tension that seemed to accompany them every time they appeared.

Finishing her breakfast, she returned to the guest apartment and saw that Ethan's door was still closed. She didn't wake him. The words 'bear' and 'sore head' came to mind, and she knew she was better off keeping her distance. Yet again she questioned whether their relationship still had any mileage left in it. After ironing her dress, she went down to the recording studio to take a closer look at the gear with which she would be working.

The recording equipment was high class although, in this digital age, Steph marvelled that Keith had chosen to include traditional gear alongside digital. Nowadays artists could get amazing results with a computer and some fancy software for a fraction of the cost of equipping an old-style studio, but of course cost wasn't a problem for Keith. The console itself was in pristine condition and without any of the coffee stains or scratches that decorated their battered one in London. In fact, this one looked as if it had never been used. There was even a hefty instruction manual lying on top of it which had barely been opened. The chairs at the console and the high stools in the performance area looked brand new and one still had a tag hanging from it.

The audio equipment was top of the range and there was a sparkling new piano keyboard on one side of the performance area together with a drum set and three guitars, amplifiers and a range of speakers. In particular Steph's eyes were drawn to a guitar she recognised as Keith's famous silver Stratocaster that would probably fetch a million dollars if he ever decided to sell it. Considering the studio wasn't even locked, this place was a potential goldmine for any would-be burglar. No wonder the villa had high fences, security cameras and live-in custodians in the shape of Cesare and Donatella.

Steph spent a happy hour fiddling with the equipment, familiarising herself with it all before deciding that as it was almost eleven and Ethan still hadn't appeared, she would make a bit of noise in the hope that it would filter up the stairs and wake him. She set the console to record and went over to the brand-new keyboard. The tone was perfect, and it offered a multitude of settings. Although she could have cranked it up to full church organ mode and blown Ethan out of bed, she kept it in traditional piano and settled down to play Chopin's *Fantaisie-Impromptu*, which she loved. As always, she lost herself in her playing and didn't hear the door open until she came to the end of the piece and was roused from her reverie by the sound of clapping. She looked up to see Keith standing there.

'Brilliant, Steph. I didn't realise you were a classical pianist.'

She felt herself blushing. 'I was doing a sound test and I needed something I could record so that I could play around with it. Now that you're here, I don't suppose you could give me a few bars of whatever appeals to you on the guitar?'

'Of course, but why don't you play me something else first? How about modern stuff? Do you play that as well?'

'To be honest, I grew up playing all your hits. If you promise not to laugh, I could have a go at one...' And she launched into the piano solo from 'Getting Back on Top', one of Royalty's early hit singles. She had learnt it by ear, after religiously studying a VHS cassette of Vince Dutton, the group's now long-dead keyboard player, performing it. She had played the video over and over again until the tape actually snapped, but by that time she had mastered the tune. It was a difficult piece, and she was delighted to get through it this morning without any serious hiccups. Keith applauded her once more.

'Terrific, Steph. Vince would have been impressed.'

'Thanks, Keith. It was so sad about him. I was so sorry when I heard the news.'

His expression became more sombre. 'It was a tragedy for him and for all of us.'

It was on the tip of Steph's tongue to quiz him about the current status of the group but before she could utter a word, Ethan appeared in the doorway looking like a refugee from a zombie apocalypse. His long hair was normally fairly unruly, but today it looked as though he'd been out in a hurricane.

'Keith, hi. Sorry I'm a bit late this morning. Must have overslept.' He was wearing the same clothes as the previous day and in all probability, he had been wearing them all night. Keith took a couple of steps back when he saw him but didn't comment on his appearance or his alcohol intake the previous night.

'Hi, Ethan. No problem. Your recording engineer's just been giving me a private concert; and a very good one at that.'

Steph was quick to explain. 'I needed a bit of music I could record and play back so I could spend a bit of time fiddling with all the gizmos on Keith's amazing equipment.'

'Let's see how it sounds.' Ethan headed for the console and slumped into one of the new chairs. 'Keith, if you feel like playing something, I'd like to try laying down a track or two so that, like Steph says, we can play around with it and use that to familiarise ourselves with everything your gear can do. Acoustic or electric, you decide.'

Steph was relieved to hear him sounding authoritative, even if he did look as though he had just crawled out of bed. She sat down in the other chair, and they looked on as Keith picked up an acoustic guitar.

'I'll give you a few snippets of some of the new songs I've written. See what you think.'

In all, he played for about twenty minutes while Ethan supervised the recording and occasionally gave an order to step back from the mike or to lean in. It was all very informal, almost as if Keith was on stage and they were part of a very intimate audience. By the time he finished playing, Steph was getting a very good feeling about the chances of success for the new album. What she had just heard was unmistakably still Royalty, but with a softer, more mature feel to it and she felt sure the public would love it.

She certainly did.

Chapter 5

Lunch was a cold buffet on the terrace with a delicious selection of antipasti, salads and cold fish and meat dishes. Steph helped herself to a plate of salad, a handful of prawns and some fresh soft goat's cheese. When she took it back to the table, Faye looked across at her accusingly.

'Is that all you're having? You'll fade away and die if you don't eat.'

Sky nudged Steph with her elbow. 'Don't listen to Mum, she's always trying to get me to eat more too.'

Steph grinned at both of them. 'Thanks, Faye, but this'll be great. I'm saving myself for tonight. When I took the iron back to Donatella she told me she's doing pizza for dinner. I love pizza and I haven't had an authentic Italian one since before my dad died so I need to save room for it.'

They all sat around a single big table and Steph found herself between Sky on one side of her and Ben on the other. In spite of his haggard look, she couldn't help feeling a little thrill of excitement and she just wished she could record this moment and somehow send it back to her teenage self to let her know that dreams really did come true. Although he didn't say much to her, she felt comfortable in his company as, in fact, she did with all of them now that Denver and Willow had gone off to Florence for the day.

She enjoyed chatting to Sky, who told her about her up-coming wedding in mid-December. This was to be held in an old manor house in the Cotswolds and Steph wondered if it would be a glittering showbiz affair. It turned out Sky was only two years older than she was; just about to turn thirty-two, and they had a lot in common. Sky had a job in marketing but she had grown up playing the guitar and although she claimed to have got rusty over the years it was clear that the Bailey family had music in their blood. She was good company and Steph began to strike up a real friendship with her.

After lunch the guests gradually retired to their rooms or to the pool – Ethan was hopefully heading for the shower and a change of clothes – until Steph found herself alone with Faye. They chatted easily and Steph gently enquired about the reason why the relationship between Denver and Sky appeared to be strained and maybe also with her other son, Robert, the owner of Waldorf the Labrador. The answer was edifying.

'There's always been friction between the three of them and if I'm honest, most of it has come from Denver.' Faye sighed. 'I think much of the problem stems from the fact that Den's their half-brother. His mother was Keith's first wife, and that marriage didn't last long.'

This was news to Steph. 'What happened? Did they divorce?'

'No, she just disappeared one day, leaving the toddler behind. Keith didn't hear a word from her for days until news arrived that she'd gone off with the drummer from another group. Only a matter of weeks later she was killed along with all the members of that group in a plane crash. I don't know if you heard about it.'

The details of the horror crash in the Rocky Mountains came back to Steph, even if she hadn't realised that Keith's first wife had been among the victims. 'Wow, that must have been tough on Keith, and tough on Denver growing up without a mum.'

'It certainly was awful for both of them. I met Keith a couple of years later. I was working as a nurse in Bournemouth, and one of my friends was going out with a musician. I went with her to a party and quite literally bumped into Keith. He was blind drunk and he almost knocked me down the stairs. As it was, he banged his head, I bandaged him up, and the rest, as they say, is history. One thing led to another, and he and I got together, and the result was Sky, followed by Rob – with a wedding ceremony somewhere in the middle.'

'And you took on little Denver as well.'

'Of course. He was only five when I first saw him and, although I've tried my hardest, we've never really hit it off. My therapist tells me she thinks he subconsciously blames me for his mother's death. Alternatively, it's just jealousy that his father moved on and settled down with me. Whatever it is, there's always been tension between the two of us, and Den's never got on very well with the other two. Sky's a strong character – of course she's a woman and we're way tougher than men – and she's always been able to handle him, but Rob struggles.' She glanced around discreetly before continuing. 'Den can be a bully and Rob's never been able to break out of it. That's why he keeps himself to himself when his big brother's about.'

'You said Robert lives here now. Do Sky and Denver still live at home with you?'

'God, no. Sky would scratch Den's eyes out if they did – if Keith didn't throttle him first.' She shuddered. 'Den's now moved to California, and that's been a liberation for all of us. Sky and Tom are in Manchester, and she rarely sees her big brother, which is no bad thing. As for Rob, he's only too happy to stay well out of the way here in Italy.'

'So we won't be seeing Robert as long as his brother's here?'

'It's probably for the best. They only fight otherwise. Rob's quite happy, especially since he got Waldorf.'

'Man's best friend…'

That evening, before dinner, Steph had a chance to chat to Ben's wife, Lottie, and what she learnt about her teenage crush was instructive. Lottie confirmed that he had been struggling with a serious drug problem for years and had done no fewer than four sessions in rehab. Three times he had relapsed afterwards but the last time it had finally worked, and he had now been clean for over two years. The fact that he had been a bit dozy the previous day was because he had been having trouble sleeping recently and was just feeling tired. Nothing more sinister. Hopefully this holiday would do him a lot of good.

Lottie waited until Keith and Johnny embarked on their pre-dinner concert before carrying on with her tale. Ben was just looking on like the previous night and Lottie explained his hesitation. 'He's taking it a day at a time – we both are – but so far so good. I have no idea whether he'll be able to summon up the courage to start playing with the others again, but I live in hope. It's so sad to see the toll addiction has taken on him. Do you realise? He's two years younger than me, but sometimes I think he looks more like my dad.'

Steph was quick to offer reassurance. 'He doesn't look that old. It's just the grey hair.' Although they both knew it wasn't just that. 'He was looking good at lunchtime, and I can see a difference in him already after just one day.' At that moment Keith and Johnny finished their version of Bon Jovi's 'Livin' on a Prayer' and launched into another of their old Royalty hits but still, Ben remained a bystander. He made no attempt to join in but neither Keith nor Johnny tried to force him. Once they had started again, Steph queried this with Lottie.

'Hasn't he been playing? Is he out of practice?'

Lottie shook her head. 'Very much the opposite. He spends hours every day playing his guitar.' She gave Steph a wry smile. 'He calls his favourite guitar Clarabelle, and I sometimes feel quite jealous. He spends more time with her than with me.'

'So why do you think he doesn't want to join in?'

The smile slipped from Lottie's face. 'He's been that way ever since Vince died. He's never been able to explain it completely, but I think he feels he was at least partly responsible for Vince's death – you know, because of the drugs they were taking together – and he can't handle the idea of the group without Vince in it.' She glanced around again. 'The thing is that there was a lot of trouble in the band back then. Keith was throwing his weight around and Ben was close to walking away when Vince killed himself. I sometimes wonder if Ben hadn't been thinking along the same lines too.'

'When you say, "throwing his weight around", what do you mean? Keith seems a pacific sort of guy.'

'He's a lot better now, but back then he was a tyrant. He's ten years older than the others and he thought of himself as the main man, the leader of the group, and he felt he should be making all the decisions and giving the others orders. I'm not saying he was responsible for what Vince did, but his constant shouting at him probably didn't help.'

'That's so awful. So Ben's worried Keith might start screaming and shouting all over again and that's why he's holding back? What a shame. I'm sure he'd enjoy it if he could find the courage to try again.'

'I know you're right, but it's been ten years now and he still hasn't changed his mind. Mind you, just getting him to agree to come over here now was a major victory and it shows he's making progress. He and Keith have even been chatting together a bit, so it looks as though they might be getting back to being friends again. Here's hoping. I know it would do Ben a world of good.'

A few moments later Denver and Willow arrived back from their trip to Florence. He appeared far happier than the previous night, although his girlfriend was still looking daggers at Steph. He came over and bent down to kiss Faye on the cheeks. From the expression of surprise on her face, this wasn't a common occurrence.

'*Ciao*, how're you doing?' He was sounding very relaxed, suspiciously relaxed, and the thought crept into Steph's head that this bonhomie might be chemically induced. She hadn't seen a single trace of drugs among the group members so far, but her suspicions grew as he came over and hugged Lottie and then did the same to Steph herself. She shied back from his touch and the first thing she saw was Willow, looking as though she was about to launch herself across the table at her. To defuse the situation Steph jumped to her feet and glanced at her watch.

'Seven o'clock. I told my mum I'd call her. Do excuse me.' And she hurried out into the sunset and down the steps to the path leading to the beach. When she got there, she perched on the big flat boulder and took a few deep breaths. Two thoughts were going through her head, neither of them welcome.

Uppermost in her mind was the unwanted attention she was receiving from the son of the man who was paying for her to be here. If she were to follow her instincts and tell him to take a hike, this might lead to a major scene, and there might even be a chance that she might find herself on a flight back to London. And the logical corollary to this would be that it might also see her lose the job she loved. Ethan could hardly keep working with Royalty if the 'right-hand woman' he was employing was considered persona non grata by them. She groaned to herself as the shadows lengthened and was on the point of phoning her mum to ask for her advice when the sound of splashing attracted her attention. Coming through the water towards her in the twilight were two heads; one canine and one human. As she looked on, two figures emerged from the water, and she gulped.

It wasn't quite the same as the moment Daniel Craig emerged from the water in whichever Bond film it was, but it was pretty special all the same. As the man walked out of the sea with water streaming down his body, she felt a totally unexpected shiver of attraction. There was something about the sight of this tall, athletic man that reached deep inside her, and it wasn't a feeling she had ever experienced as forcibly before.

She didn't have time to let her mind dwell on the implications of this as the Labrador came bounding across the beach towards her, tail wagging furiously. Realising that the dog was as soaking wet as the man, she hastily scrambled up until she was standing on the rock so Waldorf could only prod her feet with his nose, rather than fling himself at her and soak yet another outfit, albeit just shorts and a T-shirt this time.

'*Waldorf, vieni qui!*'

The command did the trick and the dog turned away and hurried back to his master who was standing stock still, looking puzzled, midway between the sea and Steph's boulder, now gripping the excited dog's collar in one hand and studying her intently. Realising who this man was, even though his face was in the shadows, she scrambled down from her perch on the rock and walked across to greet him.

'Hi, you must be Robert. My name's Steph. I'm the recording engineer. We're here to get your father's studio working.' She, too, carefully avoided any mention of a possible new Royalty album. She now knew that this was a taboo subject.

'Hi.' Not the longest of utterances but coupled by the touch of his wet fingers as they shook hands, it still succeeded in reproducing that same seismic tremor throughout her body. She found she had to clear her throat before saying anything else.

'Been for a swim?' As openers went, this was without doubt one of the more inane, and the moment it popped out she was glad of the shadows to hide her blushes. What on earth was going on inside her? She sounded like a teenager.

'Yes.' There was a brief pause before he gave a little wave of the hand. 'Bye.'

And he and his dog headed off up the path leaving her feeling more confused than she had felt for ages. She was still in a relationship with Ethan and yet she hadn't been able to suppress a feeling of attraction for this other man. She was going to have to be very careful.

–

She was still feeling confused an hour later when she returned to the villa for dinner. The others were all already seated around the table and she slipped into the last spare seat, fortunately at the other end, as far away from Denver as possible, although this meant she was alongside Ethan. Johnny and his wife Tara were opposite her and they gave her a smiley welcome. Ethan was clutching a glass in his hand, but she was relieved to see that it contained water this time. He turned his head towards her as she sat down.

'Did you talk to your mum?'

'Yes.' She didn't tell him what they had talked about. Her doubts about Ethan himself would not make suitable dinner table conversation. 'She sends her love.' She hadn't.

'Yeah, right...' Ethan had no illusions. 'Anyway, listen: Johnny's been telling me that he and Keith are coming down to the studio tomorrow at ten to lay down a track or two. You'd better be wide awake and bring your A game.'

Biting her tongue to stifle a retort, she smiled sweetly. 'Yes, boss. Of course.'

Johnny chimed in from across the table. 'Hey, Steph, Keith tells me you're a classically trained pianist. That's great. You'll have to play us something one of these days.'

She smiled back at him. 'Not really classically trained, I'm afraid. I did all the piano grades at school and a degree in music, but I'm nothing like concert pianist level. I just don't have the dedication. I love playing, but I couldn't imagine a life where I have to sit at a keyboard on my own every day and practise for hours on end, repeating the same stuff over and over again.'

'Like Rob does.' Tara looked as if she had caught the sun today. Her face was peppered with freckles and her cheeks were flushed. 'Faye tells me he practises for hours and hours. In fact, she says if you go down to the beach you can sometimes hear his beautiful violin music coming from his house on the cliff top.'

'Keith said he was good. Does he play with an orchestra?'

'He's better than that. He's really famous now as a soloist.'

Steph still maintained a keen interest in classical music, but the name Robert Bailey didn't ring any bells.

Noticing her uncertainty, Tara went on to explain. 'He's always used Faye's maiden name: Sinclair.'

'Rob Sinclair!' The penny dropped. 'He's Rob Sinclair? Wow. He's extremely well known. But why not use his real surname?'

Tara shot a glance down the table to check that they weren't being overheard. 'Faye says it's because he wanted to make it on his own merits, not as the son of a music legend like Keith.' She winked. 'Unlike his big brother...'

Steph sat back and digested what she had just heard. One thing was for sure: if she ever had the opportunity to listen in to one of Robert's practice sessions she would jump at the chance. Had her father still been alive, he, too, would have been delighted to have that opportunity. Nostalgic thoughts of her father, immediately followed by worry about her mammogram results, darkened her mood, but she was shaken out of her melancholy by the arrival of Donatella with a trolley load of antipasti. Tonight these included slices of red peppers, roasted and skinned and then rolled around small anchovy fillets laced with olive oil and garlic. They were exceptional. As they helped themselves to these and other delicacies, Cesare came around to ask how they would like their pizzas. Steph decided to stick with the fishy theme and opted for what he called a *pizza ai frutti di mare*, which would apparently be topped with all sorts of seafood.

Beside her, Ethan appeared to be controlling his drinking a lot better than the previous night; no doubt aware of the importance of being at his best the next morning. Thoughts of the recording session to come made her ask Johnny for his take on Ben's hesitation to get involved with the band once more. She was careful to check that Ben himself was out of earshot further up the table before doing so.

'Is it just going to be you and Keith tomorrow morning? No Ben?'

Johnny shook his head. 'Not so far as I know.' He, too, checked that they weren't being overheard before continuing. 'Lottie says he plays his guitar every day and, if anything, he's even better now than he used to be, so I don't think it's a confidence thing. I think it's just a hangover to what happened ten years ago.' He raised an eyebrow towards her. 'You know all about that, I imagine.'

'I know Vince died. I read that it was drugs.'

'It was drugs all right. He was completely out of it. In fact, he'd been getting worse and worse. On stage we had to have a second keyboard player in the background to cover for him. We actually unplugged him from the amp on more than one occasion and he didn't even notice. He could hardly stand up unsupported at the end.' He shook his head sadly. 'There was only one way it was going to end… and it did.'

'And Ben was so affected by his death that he opted out of the band there and then?'

'That's right. Now, ten years on, Keith and I think the time's right for us to reform before we get too old, but Ben's still very hesitant.'

'Lottie said Keith had been getting a bit too bossy, and Ben's maybe afraid that'll all start up again.'

'He certainly was bossy back then – and I can think of a few less polite words to describe him – but I'm getting the distinct impression he's mellowed since.' Johnny shot her a little grin. 'And if he hasn't, then Ben might not be the only one not signing up again.'

Steph nodded slowly. There was a lot hanging on how the next few days panned out. It certainly didn't look as though Royalty reforming was anything like a done deal yet. She offered a bit of encouragement. 'Like I say, Keith's been fine since we got here, hasn't he, Ethan? He played us a few bits of his new stuff this morning and we loved it.'

Ethan joined in. 'You never know, once Ben hears what you and Keith can produce, maybe he'll feel like joining in.'

'That's what we're hoping, but neither of us is holding our breath.'

The pizzas arrived and, as expected, were amazing. They were so big that they spilled out over the sides of the already extra-large plates, but the base and crust was wonderfully thin and perfectly cooked, and Steph surprised herself by managing to eat virtually the whole thing. Afterwards, when Donatella arrived with the offer of chocolate and raspberry tart, all Steph could do was to shake her head weakly and compliment her on the pizza. Later on, as Donatella and Cesare were clearing the table, Steph approached them for help.

'Keith and Faye have their anniversary on Friday, haven't they? They've been so terribly kind and welcoming to me, I'd like to get them something and I wondered if you had any ideas. They've probably already got everything they could possibly need and I don't want to give them something useless or tacky.'

Cesare and his wife had a quick confab before Cesare produced a suggestion. 'I'm going down to Lerici tomorrow afternoon to pick up supplies. Why don't you come down with me and see if you can find something in the local shops? You're right about Keith and Faye already having all they want, but you might spot something and, if not, flowers are always safe.'

The party broke up at eleven, and Ethan accompanied Steph back to the guest apartment down the path between the cactus and palm trees. She was pleased to see that tonight he was looking and sounding sober. She was even beginning to wonder whether this more responsible behaviour might herald the long-awaited change in him for which she had been hoping, when he suddenly stopped dead and turned towards her.

'So it's all over between us, then? Is that right?'

To give herself time, she threw a question back at him. 'What makes you say that?'

'It's been getting worse and worse of late. You're always going on at me: "Ethan, don't go out with your mates; Ethan, you drink too much; Ethan, whose bag of coke's that?" That sort of thing. And now, just in case I hadn't realised how you felt, you even refuse to share a room with me. So it's all over then?'

Steph was thinking desperately. If she said yes, might this lead to him telling her to look for another job? Alternatively, if she said no, would she find herself back in the same old round of drunken nights, embarrassing encounters and maybe even abusive behaviour? After a few seconds' pause she decided to tell him the truth, whatever the consequences.

'I'll be quite honest, Ethan, I've been thinking about this a lot. You've been behaving more and more selfishly lately, and unless that changes, you're probably right and we should split up. The thing is, you weren't always like this. Why can't you just turn back into the nice guy you used to be? Would that be so hard?'

'I'm still a nice guy.' He had stopped alongside a lamp, and she thought she spotted a chastened look on his face, but it didn't last more than a second or two before he went back on the offensive. 'But what right have you got to tell me how I should live my life?'

'If you're the other half of a relationship I'm in, then I think I have every right. If we aren't in a relationship, then of course your life's your own. I loved you a lot, Ethan; I still do, deep down. But you've changed and I like the new Ethan a whole lot less than the old one.' She waved a large moth away from her face. 'So it's your call: I want you the way you used to be. If you don't want to make the effort then you're right, and we're finished.' She turned away from the light and set off for the apartment. 'Why don't you think it over and let me know in the morning?'

Chapter 6

The recording session next morning went remarkably well, considering Steph hadn't slept much. She had had a broken night filled with thoughts of Ethan: how he used to be, as compared to how he was now, and how things might turn out between them. By the time the session started, her mind was partly on the job and partly on what Ethan had said to her after breakfast. Put simply, he had told her quite harshly that he had slept on it and that his life was his own and he would behave any way he wished. If she wanted the relationship to progress, she would just have to accept that. Stifling her disappointment and hurt, her reply had been short and to the point.

'I made my position clear last night. The choice was yours and you've chosen to stay as you are. I told you I don't want a relationship with the new Ethan so, as far as I'm concerned, it's all over between us.' Taking a deep breath, she had then asked the question that had been burning her up all night. 'Does this mean I should start looking for a new job?'

His response had been reassuring, at least in the short term. 'You're good at your job, very good. I wouldn't want to lose you. Let's just hope that things don't get weird between us.' He paused for thought. 'Probably just as well if we don't say anything to anybody here about this. Okay?'

'Okay by me.'

As she waited for Keith and Johnny to come down to the studio, Steph busied herself playing with the equipment, some of it familiar, some brand new. With the experience she had already accumulated, she soon sorted out how it all worked and set about making the usual preparations for a recording session but, as she worked, she was turning things over and over in her head.

So this was how their three-year relationship had ended; with a whimper rather than a bang. It felt somehow unreal. A short conversation and that was that; no pyrotechnics, no tears, no visible heartache on either side, whatever she might be feeling on the inside. To a neutral onlooker, nothing had changed. They were both still living in the guest apartment, they would be in close daily contact, and they would still be working together. What the neutral onlooker couldn't see was the cold void this had left in her stomach. Things had been building to a head, yes, but there had still been a part of her that had been hoping he would do the right thing and make the choice to return to being the man she had fallen for. But such was not the case, and the extra complication now was whether she was going to be able to carry on working with the man she had once loved. Only time would tell.

Keith and Johnny, unaware of the turmoil going on inside her head, came along as promised and performed two brand new numbers. Without a keyboard and a bass player, it sounded a bit hollow, but the underlying melodies were catchy and Keith's lyrics and his voice, remarkably moving. The very good news was that Keith didn't once try to put his foot down or call the shots. Hopefully this was a good sign for the future of the band. After the two men had gone off for a coffee, she and Ethan added a pretty good approximation of a bass track to the first song and she played around, improvising the sort of accompaniment on the keyboard that she thought Vince might have produced. By the time Keith and Johnny reappeared just before lunch, Ethan was able to play them the result of their efforts and it was greeted with what looked and sounded like genuine enthusiasm.

'Ethan, Steph, that's brilliant!' Keith glanced across at Johnny. 'What do you think, Johnny?'

'Amazing. Steph, you play so well. It was almost like hearing Vince himself. I'll be honest, it gave me goose-bumps.'

'It could do with some backing singers and, of course, a real bass track, but you could have a winner here.' Ethan was sounding equally enthusiastic.

'What do you think Ben will make of it?' Steph's cheeks were still blushing at the compliments.

'First we've got to get him to listen to it.' Keith shook his head slowly. 'He's still seriously uptight and I'm desperate not to frighten him off. We're going to have to take it one step at a time.'

'Why don't we try to get him down here on his own one of these days?' Steph was thinking out loud, but she saw both men nod in unison.

'That's a good idea. Why don't you or Ethan talk to him, but take it easy with him?' Keith sounded animated. 'Maybe suggest he comes and plays you something? And then when you've got him here, you could let him hear this. See what he says.'

'I think it's a great idea, but it won't be easy.' Johnny caught Steph's eye. 'It's like fly fishing. You've got to drop the fly and let it float past the trout, attracting its attention in the hope that it'll bite, but without scaring it off. Go ahead and try, but tread carefully.'

Lunch was marred by an argument between Denver and his sister. It had all been going very smoothly, with everybody agreeing that Donatella's homemade lasagne was excellent, when Steph heard raised voices at the far end of the table. It appeared that Sky had taken exception to something her brother had said.

'So Mum and Dad gave me a car for my birthday, so what?' She was staring him down. 'I didn't ask for it. It was a present. Have you got that? A present, an unsolicited gift. All right?'

'Unsolicited!' Denver almost spat the word. 'You're always scrounging off Mum and Dad.'

'*Me*… scrounging?' Sky's voice went up a couple of octaves. 'There's only one scrounger around here and it's you. Maybe if you got yourself a real job instead of pretending you can make it as a singer…'

'I *am* making it as a singer. I bet I make a damn sight more than you do.'

'Maybe, but you also spend ten times as much as I do.'

'Hey, calm down, you two. We're trying to have a nice quiet lunch here.' Keith raised both hands to the heavens. 'Couldn't you just *pretend* to get along while we're here. It's going to be our anniversary in a few days' time. Let's try and make it a happy one.'

'Your anniversary, not mine.' Denver's voice was a snarl, and Steph saw Keith's face flush.

'What the hell's that supposed to mean, Den?' Keith stared hard at his son.

'You know exactly what I mean.'

'Oh, just grow up, will you.' The expression on Keith's face was one of disbelief and barely concealed anger.

Denver stood up so sharply that his chair fell over backwards. Flinging his napkin onto the tabletop, he turned and disappeared back into the house. There was silence around the table for several seconds before Willow got to her feet and hurried off after him. Sky took a big swig of water and Tom wrapped a comforting arm around her shoulders. Steph dropped her head and hastened to finish her lasagne, determined to get away from a family tiff that was none of her business. Presumably Denver's anger stemmed from the fact that his own mother had only been married to his father for a matter of months. Steph was still eating when she heard Faye's voice.

'Sorry, everybody. You'll have to excuse Denver. He's been under a lot of pressure lately. He'll calm down.'

Steph carried on eating, wondering what sort of pressure the rich son of a mega-rich father might have. She was just finishing her food and reaching for her glass of wine when Keith stood up.

'Sorry, guys. I think it's time I spoke to my son. Enjoy the rest of your meal. Ethan, Steph, why don't you take the afternoon off, and we'll meet back in the studio later on, say five, five thirty?'

–

Cesare and Steph drove into Lerici just after three. On the way they chatted about the scenery, the weather and their respective jobs, but neither of them raised the subject of today's big row at the lunch table. That was strictly Bailey family business. As Cesare threaded his way through the narrow, crowded streets, they passed a Hotel Shelley, a Trattoria Byron and a Caffè dei Poeti. Clearly Lerici was proud of its literary heritage and not ashamed of flaunting it. Cesare managed to squeeze into a tight parking space in one of the side streets where he told her they had just one hour before the traffic wardens would pounce. After arranging to meet back at the car no later than four thirty, he went off to pick up the bits of shopping he needed while Steph wandered down to the seafront.

Although the main Italian holiday month of August was over, the town was still very busy, and she could only imagine the chaos and confusion there must be here at the height of the summer. When she reached the water, it was to find it almost completely carpeted with boats. There were sailing boats of all sizes, speedboats and larger luxury yachts moored in the huge marina or anchored out in the bay. Over to the left was the imposing castle on the rocky headland, while a large grey warship was making its way over to the naval base at La Spezia several miles to the north. It was a busy, vibrant place and very different from the peace and quiet – when not interrupted by family arguments – of Keith and Faye's hideaway barely a handful of kilometres along the coast to the south of here.

Aware that she only had limited time, Steph set off to find an anniversary present for her hosts and another 'smart' dress for herself. It took almost the whole hour, but she finally emerged from the shops with a lovely sea blue and white striped dress, a new pair of shorts, a couple of tops and, remarkably, a vintage grey T-shirt advertising the Royalty tour of Italy in 2007. As far as a present for Keith and Faye was concerned, she found a pair of wisteria plants in a pot, their young branches lovingly entwined, one hung with a simple pink ribbon and the other a light blue one. The florist had even managed to produce a bow with *Buon Anniversario* on it.

It wasn't the easiest of things to carry and she was relieved to find an ice-cream parlour only a few doors up from where the car was parked where she could set her purchases down and sit at a table on the pavement and wait for Cesare. While waiting, she ordered a bowl of apricot, dark chocolate, and meringue ice cream which tasted every bit as good as it looked.

As she savoured the ice cream, she let her mind roam and thought, yet again, of Ethan and the end of their three-year liaison. To say she had mixed feelings was to understate the confusion in her head. She had been fond of him for a long time, and it was sad to see the relationship splutter to an end in this way. Although things had been building towards a showdown, the knowledge that it was now over was unsettling, particularly as they would still be working closely together. The great unknown was how that would pan out.

At the same time she kept thinking back to the effect the appearance of Robert had had on her last night when he had emerged from the sea with his dog. She couldn't escape the fact that she had found Keith and Faye's younger son unexpectedly appealing but, even though she was now no longer emotionally linked to Ethan, she knew she would do well to stay clear of someone like Robert for two reasons.

Firstly, because he was rich and famous. Enviable as it might appear from the outside, she felt sure there was no place for somebody 'ordinary' like her in an environment where people gave each other cars as birthday presents and lived in multi-million-pound villas.

Secondly, and more importantly, she was well aware of Rob Sinclair's reputation – but not as a violinist. The tabloids were full of photos of him with an ever-changing panoply of beautiful women. She had even read an article in *La Stampa* in which the writer accused him of trying to emulate his violin-playing hero, Paganini, whose reputation as a *donnaiolo*, or womaniser, had scandalised audiences back in the eighteen hundreds. She had no intention of joining the ranks of this modern-day Paganini's cast-offs. She remembered that Paganini had been one of her father's idols, but no doubt this had been because of his prowess as a musician rather than his amorous activities.

'*Ciao*, Stefania. Look who I've bumped into.'

Her mind had been so far away as she finished her ice cream, absently staring into the middle distance, that she didn't notice Cesare until he spoke to her – in Italian as was their custom. She looked up to see him standing alongside her table with another figure behind him. He stepped to one side and Steph realised that his companion was none other than the man she had just been thinking about: Robert Bailey, aka the virtuoso violinist Rob Sinclair, a womaniser to be avoided like the plague. Taking a deep breath, she rose to her feet as Cesare made the introductions.

'Stefania, this is Robert, Signor Keith's other son. I don't know if you've met him before.'

Struggling to sound relaxed, Steph gave them both a smile and answered. 'Yes. Robert and I met briefly last night.' She switched to English. 'Isn't your lovely dog with you today?' She was relieved to hear that the butterflies that had started flitting about in her stomach didn't appear to have transferred to her voice. As she addressed him, a puzzled air appeared on his face.

'Not today.' Once again all she managed to get out of him was little more than a monosyllabic reply. Before she could ask for more, he switched to Italian and returned his attention to Cesare, avoiding looking at her, even though it was her question he was answering.

'I left Waldorf at the villa with Donatella. It's too crowded here in town, and he isn't used to being on a lead.' His Italian was impeccable. 'He has an unfortunate habit of sticking his nose into places that he shouldn't. Anyway, I'm sure you need to get on.' As far as Steph was concerned, he couldn't have made it any clearer that he wanted to get away from *her* as soon as he could. Although this tied in with what she had just been thinking, it was somehow galling to find that this well-known womaniser wasn't interested in her. Okay, so she wasn't rich or a celebrity, but it would have been good to see at least *some* attraction on his part.

Fortunately, before the conversation could get any more awkward, Steph noticed something. Her eyes were drawn a bit further up the road to where a woman in uniform was working her way down the row of parked cars towards them. 'Isn't that a traffic warden, Cesare?'

'It certainly is. Well spotted. We need to go. Roberto, do you need a lift? How did you get here? On foot?'

A look of what could only be relief spread across Robert's face as he shook his head. 'No, I came on the bike. Off you go before you get a fine.'

'See you at the weekend for the boat trip.'

Robert's face fell. 'Afraid so. *Ciao.*'

All he produced was the slightest wave of the hand and Steph was left feeling a bit miffed, even if she had managed to drag another three whole words out of him. She reminded herself that after the Ethan debacle the last thing she wanted was any kind of involvement with another man – particularly one with a reputation like Rob

74

Sinclair's – but surely just common courtesy should have made him exchange a few more words with her. Even if he didn't fancy her, he could have been a bit friendlier, couldn't he?

On the way back to the villa she was sorely tempted to ask Cesare what reason Robert might have for ignoring her in this way, but she bit her tongue and decided to say nothing for fear of putting Cesare into the uncomfortable position of having to discuss yet another one of his employers' sons. Instead, she asked about Keith and Faye's anniversary party on Friday, and he explained that it was to be a celebratory cruise across the bay past La Spezia towards the romantic little town of Portovenere with a picnic on the island of Palmaria. Steph had never heard of either and Cesare told her she had a treat in store.

'Portovenere's a kaleidoscope of colours. It has to be one of the most picturesque places on the Italian coast. Mind you, it's become unbelievably expensive. My brother-in-law used to live there, but he sold up and moved to La Spezia where he got an apartment twice as big for half the cost.'

'And the island?'

'The part where we're going should be completely deserted. Hopefully we'll have the place to ourselves. Don't forget to bring your swimming things. You enjoy swimming, don't you?'

'It's about the only exercise I do regularly. Mind you, back home it's just in the local swimming baths. Swimming in the sea's a real treat for me.'

'Robert does a lot of swimming. He swims all year round.'

With an effort, Steph did her best to banish from her mind the image of Robert emerging from the sea dripping wet, and ended up quizzing Cesare about him all the same. 'What about him? I gather there's bad blood between him and his brother and that's why he hasn't been eating with us. I suppose he has to come on Sunday, even if Denver's going to be there, doesn't he?' She could have added 'even if *I'm* going to be there', judging by Robert's attitude towards her but, once again, she steered clear of putting Cesare on the spot.

She saw him nod. 'I'm sure he will come, for his parents' sake, but you could see that he isn't looking forward to it. As soon as Denver and his... lady arrived, Robert stopped coming up to the villa.' He shook his head ruefully. 'He and his brother have been at it like cats and dogs since before I first met them. The signora says it's a feud that goes back to their childhood.'

'But on Sunday they'll both be in the same boat for a full day. Let's see how that works out.'

Chapter 7

Later that afternoon, Johnny and Keith came down to the studio and they recorded a preliminary version of another new number. To Steph's delight, the two men asked her to provide accompaniment on the keyboard and she set about trying out different dynamics as they created and refined the backing track. Although Keith occasionally interrupted and made suggestions, there was little sign of his reputed bossiness, which came as a relief. To her surprise, none of the music was written down and she was stunned to discover that Keith, who wrote most of the songs, had only the most rudimentary grasp of sheet music. Of course, she reminded herself, the Beatles, Elvis, Eric Clapton and numerous others had famously never been able to read a note.

As a result, it was very much a case of 'you hum it and I'll play it' at first, but she soon got the hang of it and spent a happy hour jamming with them until they were satisfied they had come up with the right instrumental backing to the vocals. Ethan looked on, giving occasional commands as he recorded everything, all the while subjecting Steph to looks that somehow combined appreciation along with what could have been resentment. He wasn't used to being upstaged by his recording engineer.

Still, even he had to agree that the end product after they had reworked, remixed and compressed the different layers was a song that was unmistakably vintage Royalty. All it needed now were some backing singers and a solid guitar performance from Ben, maybe with one of his famous solo riffs, to replace the generic bass track Ethan had been using for now. When they came to the end of the session and Keith and Johnny had gone off looking happy, Ethan pulled off his headphones and dropped them on the console in front of him. He ran his fingers through his hair and sat back, looking across at Steph, a peeved expression on his face.

'Keep on like this and you'll find yourself a member of Royalty.' The resentment in his voice was more noticeable now. 'You won't need me any longer. I'll have served my purpose.'

'Served your purpose?' She gave him a quizzical look.

'You know what I mean.'

'Don't tell me you're trying to say that I've been using you merely as a stepping stone to help me achieve fame and fortune.'

'Your words, not mine.'

She stood there and just stared at him in disbelief. He sounded as much a spoilt child as Denver complaining about his father's Ferrari or his sister's birthday present. 'And presumably I only hooked up with you so as to take advantage of you?' She could feel her indignation growing and was sure he must be able to hear it in her voice, so she made a conscious effort to control her already shredded emotions. 'Well, thanks, Ethan. Thanks for making me feel so much better about us breaking up. Why on earth I got together with you in the first place is a mystery to me.' With that, she turned and stormed out, resisting the temptation to slam the door behind her.

She wandered blindly down to the beach and kicked off her shoes. Although the sun was close to the horizon, the sand was still pleasantly warm, and she wandered aimlessly up and down the waterline, enjoying the feel of the sand between her toes, but barely aware of the beauty of the scene as the last remnants of a glowing red sun slowly sank below the horizon. Her head continued to spin. How Ethan could have the nerve to accuse her, after everything he had meant to her, of having used him for her own nefarious purposes like some femme fatale, was preposterous and bitterly wounding. How could he be so crass? She came close to crying for the first time that day, but she fought the temptation to sink into a pit of self-pity. Ethan, she told herself, was a jealous prat and that was that.

After a while she collected herself and went over to rest against what she was already thinking of as her boulder, her eyes staring out to sea. The sun was now little more than a minute curved strip barely visible above the horizon, sending an ever-narrowing beam of red light straight at her. She watched as her hands and legs turned crimson, then maroon until the light was extinguished and she was left in near darkness. Once again her thoughts turned to her father. She felt sure he would have been proud to know that she had been playing with such a legendary band, even if he had always claimed to have no time for modern music. He had died far too young and there was so much she wished she had said to him and never had. Her spirits sank even further and she struggled desperately to hold back the tears.

She sat there for another few minutes, the only sound the gentle sighing of the tiny waves against the sand and gradually began to consider the upside of what Ethan had said to her. Could it be that Keith and Johnny really might want her to join the group? They needed a replacement keyboard player – there was no doubt about that – but she was under no illusion that there were many thousands of keyboard players out there more talented than she would ever be. Still, she thought to herself with a burst of optimism, stranger things had happened.

She gradually became aware of the sound of a violin playing in the distance. The music coming from the cliff top to the left of her was muffled at first but then grew stronger, presumably as the violinist came outside into the evening air. She had no doubt who the musician was and she leant back and listened, enchanted, as he played a piece she instantly recognised as Massenet's beautiful *Méditation*. As the slow, haunting notes lingered over the water of the little bay she closed her eyes and let her mind empty itself of everything but the beauty of the music and the unmistakable artistry of the performer. He had the gentlest of touches, and she felt the notes resonate inside her, and as they did so, they brought back even more poignant memories of her father. When the piece came to its plaintive conclusion, and she roused herself from her dreamlike state, it was to find her cheeks running with tears. She hadn't been able to prevent herself from crying, but the experience had been cathartic and she felt somehow purged as a result.

She stayed there listening to a series of other pieces from him, culminating with Bach's unmistakable Partita in E major, whose stirring rhythm finally shook her out of her trancelike state and made her aware that it was gone eight o'clock and she was expected for dinner with the family. With real regret she wiped her eyes, slipped her sandals back on and made her way up to the villa, stopping only for a moment at her room to splash some water on her face and check that she didn't look too shell-shocked. The last thing she wanted was for Ethan to think that she had been crying over him.

Tonight's dinner was a barbecue and she helped herself to one of Donatella's homemade burgers and an ice-cold beer. The big table had been split into four smaller tables and she chose her seat strategically so as to be as far away from Ethan as possible, but seconds later realised her mistake as a familiar hand landed on her shoulder and gave it an unwelcome squeeze.

'Mind if I sit next to you?'

It was Denver and her heart sank. After all her troubles with Ethan today, the last thing she wanted was to be propositioned by this man. Still, ever conscious that she was a guest in the Bailey's house, she managed to produce a smile. 'Help yourself.'

He pulled out a chair and sat down beside her and as he did so, Willow immediately positioned herself on the other side of the table directly opposite both of them, no doubt so as to keep a close eye on any interaction between her man and Steph. As their eyes momentarily made contact, Steph could almost feel the daggers shooting towards her from the other woman.

'So what've you been doing today, Steph?' Denver picked up his burger and buried his teeth in it. Opposite him, Willow didn't appear to want to eat anything. From the look on her face, she was probably fuelled by hate.

It was an innocent enough question, so Steph told him. 'I've been down to Lerici with Cesare. It's a lovely little place, full of tourists and very busy, but still with a very Italian feel.'

'I presume you know Italy well. You certainly speak the language fluently. I've heard you talking to Cesare and Donatella. Sounded good to me.'

'I've had a lot of practice over the years. Do you speak it?' As long as he was sticking to this sort of thing, she was happy to continue the conversation with him.

He shook his head and reached for his beer. After taking a sip he answered with another shake of the head. 'I'm no good with languages. Willow is, though.' He glanced across the table. 'You speak Spanish like a native, don't you?'

'My mom's originally from Mexico. I grew up speaking it.' This was one of the first full sentences Steph had heard her utter and, deciding this was progress, she addressed Willow directly.

'Sort of like me then. My dad was Italian. That's why I speak it.'

If she had been hoping that this might mark some kind of thawing of their relationship, what Denver did next soon put paid to that. Setting down his burger, he reached across and before Steph could move out of the way, he had started stroking her arm. 'Beautiful and talented. What more could a man ask for?'

Steph was quick to retrieve her arm and wipe away the smudges of ketchup his fingers had left on her skin. Resisting the temptation to get up and move, she smiled sweetly and took refuge in subterfuge. 'Thank you. That's what my future fiancé says.'

'Your future fiancé?' This at least provoked a verbal reaction from Willow. 'You and Ethan…?'

'That's right. We had a little heart-to-heart earlier this evening.'

Willow and Denver didn't need to know the content of that conversation, and, as long as this fictitious engagement helped to keep Denver at arm's length and prevent his girlfriend from launching an all-out assault, Steph felt it was a worthwhile subterfuge. Thankfully, it appeared to work. That was the last time that Denver made any amorous advances, and as the evening progressed, they managed to carry on at least an attempt at conversation without Steph slapping him or Willow trying to stick a fork in her. The conversation led, almost inevitably, to music.

'I hear that you play piano, Steph. Are you good?' Having finished his burger, Denver was picking at the last few fries on his plate.

'I'm not in your brother's league, but I get by.'

'My brother...' Denver snorted and drank deeply from his bottle of beer. 'That bloody violin was all he ever wanted to do as a kid. He never wanted to play any games, not with me, not even with his sister. Do you know something? Rob sometimes plays his violin for four or five hours every day. That's crazy! Call that a life...?'

'At the top level you really need to be single-minded and dedicated. But if that's what he enjoys, why not? As long as his girlfriends don't mind.' She tried telling herself that she wasn't really fishing for information, but her subconscious treated that thought with the disdain it deserved.

'His girlfriends?' Denver shook his head. 'They're not around for long enough.'

'What's that supposed to mean?' Although she already knew the answer.

'He doesn't hang on to them for long enough. Use and discard is his motto. Besides, all he's really interested in is his damn violin. Inevitably the women in his life take second place.' He gave a dismissive wave of the hand and stood up. 'I need another beer. Either of you want anything?' Seeing them both shake their heads he headed for the bar.

This, of course, left Steph all alone with Willow.

The ensuing silence was deafening. Although Steph's pretence that she and Ethan were engaged had appeared to defuse at least some of Willow's animosity, the expression on the heavily made-up face opposite her had rarely progressed beyond suspicious or worse all evening. Finally, it was Willow who broke the silence.

'Den and I are going to get engaged.' It wasn't so much an announcement as a challenge, but Steph had absolutely no interest in taking it up. Denver meant nothing to her.

'I'm very happy for you.' Keen to avoid another uncomfortable silence, she continued. 'Have you been together long?'

'Two months, just over.'

Wow, Steph thought to herself, nobody could accuse Willow of being slow off the mark. Two months from nought to engagement was fast going by any standard and Steph felt what was almost a pang of pity for this almost certainly delusional woman. As she had told herself on the beach just an hour or two ago, strange things could happen but, feeling that by now she had a pretty good handle on the object of Willow's affections, Steph seriously doubted whether he was on the same wavelength. Still, what they did with their lives was nothing to do with her, so she did her best to sound supportive.

'Good for you. I wish you well.'

She was almost relieved to see Denver reappear with three bottles of beer in his hands.

'Here, I brought reinforcements. Help yourselves.'

Steph thanked him but stuck with her half-empty bottle for now. To get away from the subject of his relationship with Willow – or with her for that matter – Steph brought the subject back to music, this time Denver's variety.

'What about you, Denver? Where are you playing next? Have you got any albums coming out?' What little she knew about his music had been summed up disparagingly by Ethan as 'elevator music' and she had to confess she had never knowingly heard anything by him.

'I'm starting a season at Caesar's Palace next month. As for albums, I've got a few songs I'd like to record, but I haven't got around to it yet.' A thought must have occurred to him. 'Come to think of it, why don't I have a go at recording something while I'm here? My stuff's mostly acoustic so no need for a full backing orchestra. That way I'll have some demo stuff to give out if I meet any interesting people over there.'

By now, Steph was seriously regretting getting him onto this topic, but it was too late. The studio belonged to his father so, as long as Keith had no objections, she couldn't really say no. Although she knew she would insist on Ethan being there as well.

'That sounds interesting. Why not have a word with your dad?' No sooner had she made the suggestion than she found herself wondering whether the two of them were speaking again after Denver's flare-up at lunchtime but, from the expression on his face, that didn't look as if it was going to be a problem. Presumably they had buried the hatchet.

'Good idea.' With that, he jumped to his feet and headed off to the table where his parents were sitting.

Acutely aware that she and Willow were alone once again, Steph hurried to make conversation rather than endure another tedious silence.

'What about you, Willow? Are you musical?'

'I don't play an instrument if that's what you mean, but I sing. I met Den when we were both on the same bill in Chicago this June.'

'What sort of stuff do you sing?'

'I'm in a girl band. We don't have any records out yet, but our manager's pushing for a recording deal.' For the first time a hint of a smile appeared on the girl's face.

'Terrific. What's the name of the band? I'll look out for you.'

'We're called RBB – that's short for The Redhead, The Brunette and The Blonde. You can probably work out for yourself which one I am.'

If she were feeling catty, Steph might have suggested The Brunette in view of Willow's dark roots but, instead, she just smiled. As for RBB, Steph had never heard of them, but she was saved from having to confess this by the reappearance of Denver looking happy. 'I've spoken to Dad. He's tied up tomorrow morning, so he says the studio's all mine. What time suits you, Steph?'

She nodded reluctantly. 'I'd better ask Ethan first, but how about ten? Sound good?'

'Sounds great. I can't wait.'

It sounded terrible to Steph, but she didn't have much option.

Chapter 8

The recording session with Denver the next day turned out to be more interesting than Steph had been expecting. It didn't come as a surprise to see him arrive under the watchful eye of Willow, today wearing a skimpy garment that might have been a minute skirt or might have been a wide belt. Either way, when she perched on one of the stools in the recording area, Steph could sense a distinct increase in interest from Ethan at the console. The sight of Ethan appeared to have appeased Willow's possessive instincts as far as her boyfriend was concerned, and she almost looked happy for a change.

Denver had brought an acoustic guitar with him, and it soon turned out that he was more than competent with it. Steph wasn't quite sure what she'd been expecting but listening to him produce a professional sounding perform-ance came as something of a surprise. From Ethan's earlier disparaging comments and from Keith's apparent reluct-ance to let him play along with Johnny and him, she had been expecting far worse. As far as genre was concerned, it soon emerged that Denver preferred ballads and there was a definite Sinatra vibe to his singing. As with so many crooners, he slipped into an American accent in his songs, but he did it well and she felt sure the average man or woman in the street wouldn't have twigged that he had been brought up in the UK. Mind you, Faye had told

Steph that he was the only one in the family with a US passport, courtesy of his birth mother and being born in Denver, hence the name.

The even bigger surprise came from his partner. Although Steph provided a bit of keyboard accompaniment to his guitar playing, Ethan felt that some backing vocals would help, and Willow was quick to volunteer. The surprise came from the discovery that she had a terrific voice. Underneath the prickly outer coating, it was clear there was a lot of talent inside Willow. The combination of Denver's voice and her backing resulted in them being able to lay down a couple of decent demo tracks, although Steph wasn't sure how many people would be interested in cover versions of 'I Did It My Way' and 'Moon River'. Maybe Ethan hadn't been too far out with his 'elevator music' description.

Denver and Willow left the studio looking happy, and Steph found herself alone with Ethan for the first time since his outburst the previous night. As the silence lengthened, she worked quickly to close down the machines on which she had been working and was on the point of heading out for a pre-lunch walk or swim when he stopped her, his tone, if not fully apologetic, certainly more conciliatory.

'Listen, Steph, about what I said, I probably came across a bit hard. I'm happy for you if Royalty really do make you an offer you can't refuse, and I fully understand that you wouldn't be able to refuse it. Nobody would. I just know that I'll miss having you here alongside me.'

She was genuinely amazed. It might not have been the most eloquent of apologies, but it was a hell of a lot more than she had ever got out of him before, and she even felt a little tug on her heartstrings at his words. He presumably meant 'here alongside me' in a work sense, but it made her stop and take stock once more. Could it be that he was rethinking his refusal of her request to modify his behaviour and, if so, what did that mean as far as she was concerned, or had they both already passed the point of no return? For now, she skirted around the subject.

'It's all right, Ethan, I understand. Besides, the chances of them offering me a place in the group are next to non-existent. There are loads of far better keyboard players than me out there. But like I've told you before, I love my job and I'd also miss being here alongside you.'

He could make of that what he wanted.

It was just after twelve when she emerged from the studio and headed back to her room to change into her swimming things. It was another hot day, but clouds were massing over the hills behind the coast, and she had a feeling a change in the weather might be on the way. Still, if it did rain, this would be the first she would have seen since leaving London so she couldn't complain.

The water was as warm as ever and she had a lovely, relaxing swim. She was floating lazily on her back, watching the seagulls wheeling overhead, when she discovered she had company A snuffling sound accompanied by a few splashes and snorts were followed by the unmistakable feel of a nose against her shoulder. She straightened up, treading water, and saw the Labrador alongside her with a broad canine smile on his face.

'*Ciao, bello.*' She reached out a hand to ruffle his ears and glanced around, wondering if she would see his master, but the bay was empty apart from her and the dog. Repressing what might have been disappointment – in spite of her resolve to steer clear of Rob because of his reputation – she swam to the beach accompanied by her four-legged companion. Back on the sand the dog wasted no time in finding a suitable piece of driftwood and dropping it at her feet. She and he were still playing fetch when she heard a voice.

'Hi, Steph, looks like you've found yourself a friend.'

It was Lottie, and along with her was her husband. Both of them were wearing swimming things and both looked as though they had managed to catch a bit of sun. Ben, in particular, looked all the better for it. Steph gave them a big smile and a warning.

'Watch out when Waldorf comes back out of the water. The first thing he'll do is shake himself and soak you and then he'll probably jump all over you to say hello. He's a very friendly dog.'

It was Ben who replied. 'No problem. We love dogs. We've got three back home.' He looked and sounded bright and cheerful today.

'Who's looking after the dogs while you're here?'

'Our daughter and her husband. They've moved in with the kids to keep an eye on things while we're over here.'

At that moment the happy dog emerged from the sea and, as Steph had feared, immediately soaked Lottie and Ben as he shook himself dry. As a result, they headed for the water to clean up and cool down while Steph, who had taken evasive action, dried herself off and took up her station on her favoured rock. She had been delighted to see Ben sounding so relaxed and she wondered if this might translate into a desire to join the others in reforming Royalty.

A few minutes later Lottie and then Ben joined her on the beach while the dog trotted off up the little path towards his home. Lottie leant back against the warm rock and stretched happily. 'What a beautiful day. I can hardly believe we're here.' She glanced over at her husband. 'You needed a lot of persuading, Benny, but now I bet you're glad we came, aren't you?'

Ben nodded decisively before answering and when he spoke there was a smile on his face, and it suited him. For a moment or two, Steph was reminded of how he used to look when Royalty were in their heyday.

'I'm glad all right. The water's perfect, the private beach fantastic and this whole area's fabulous. Gulf of the Poets – I can see why they came here.' He reached across and caught hold of his wife's hand. 'Thanks, sweetie. Sorry you had to bully me into it, but I promise next time you won't have to.'

'Does this mean we're coming back?' Lottie was grinning from ear to ear, clearly delighted to see her husband looking and sounding so cheerful. Steph had the feeling he hadn't been doing a lot of smiling for quite some time.

'You know what I was thinking, Lot? How about we do like Keith's done and buy ourselves a little place over here? Would you like that?'

'Would I like that?' The expression of joy on his wife's face spoke volumes. 'I'd love that, Benny, I really would. Why don't you have a word with Keith or Cesare? They're bound to know the best places and the best agencies to contact.'

He nodded to himself a few times. 'And maybe I should build myself a little recording studio as well...'

Steph could see the amazement on his wife's face at this mention of recording and so she decided to risk a suggestion.

'If there's anything you want to know about building up a studio, I'd be happy to help.'

She was pleased and relieved to see him nod again. 'That would be great, thanks, Steph. I imagine the technology's moved on quite a bit since the last time I was in a recording studio…' His voice tailed off and Steph spotted concern on Lottie's face, but he rallied. 'Maybe you might have a few minutes one of these days to show me what sort of gear Keith's got. Would that be possible?'

'I'd be delighted. Just say the word.' Steph was celebrating internally. This was real progress. And while she had him in the studio, she toyed with the idea of playing him Keith and Johnny's demo tracks but decided it might be a bit too soon. Remembering Johnny's fishing analogy, she resolved to bide her time and see if he would rise to the bait.

–

That afternoon Steph joined Ethan in the studio to prepare for another session with Keith and Johnny. Outside, the clouds were gathering and there was an oppressive humid feel to the air. Inside, Ethan was looking unusually subdued, and she hoped he wasn't still brooding. When the two men arrived, Steph mentioned what Ben had said earlier about wanting to come down to the studio to take a look and Keith's face lit up.

'Great stuff, Steph. Just go slow with him, though. A bit at a time, okay?'

Johnny gave her a little smile and mimed slowly reeling in a fish. 'Easy does it…'

Today's session saw Keith and Johnny performing two more of the new numbers and for both of them Keith asked Steph to join in again on the keyboard. As before, Ethan and she were then able to mix the different tracks together, enhancing here and fading there until the result was impressive enough to have Keith and Johnny high-fiving each other in delight.

'If only we could get Ben on board… We really have something here.' Keith then came up with a fascinating offer. 'Steph, how would you feel about playing keyboard on all the tracks? There's no question that we need that extra instrument, and you manage to reproduce the Royalty sound so perfectly. I think you'd be great.' As if realising that he was sounding a bit too bossy, he turned to Johnny. 'What do you think, Johnny? She's what we need, isn't she?'

'Keith's right, Steph.' Johnny nodded in agreement. 'It's like having Vince back here with us.'

Keith was thinking of practical matters. 'And of course this means you'll get credit on the record and you'll get paid. So, will you do it?' He glanced across at Ethan who was standing there with an expression on his face that was hard to read. 'You don't mind if Steph helps out on the keyboard, do you?'

Ethan nodded mutely while Steph struggled to come to terms with what had just happened. Ethan's prediction had been right. She was being offered the chance to participate in a world-renowned group's new album. Considering that her last gig had been playing at an eightieth birthday party in Golders Green in exchange for little more than cake and cab fare this was an amazing step up. She could hardly control her excitement as she replied, doing her best to resist the temptation to hug both Keith and Johnny as she did so.

'If you're sure you want me, you know I'd love to. I can't think of anything better. Thank you so much.'

'That's great.' Keith gave a satisfied smile. 'In fact, if your boss can spare you today, I'd like to take you through some of the other songs I've written. Ethan, could I borrow Steph for a few hours later on?'

Again, Ethan just nodded. It was only after the two men had left the studio that he found his voice and Steph was struck by the sullen resignation in his tone. 'So that's the way it's going to go down. First you dump me and then you go off and leave me in the middle of a job.'

'I'm not leaving in the middle of the job. This *is* the job and I'm not going anywhere. Besides, haven't you ever heard about the customer always being right?'

'And you end up with a good few thou in your pocket and your name on the album cover.'

He sounded like a grumpy teenager. The softer tone of that morning was conspicuous by its absence and this sudden mood swing was unexpected and concerning. She decided to reply in kind.

'And your name'll be on there as well, and you'll be well paid. And of course I had to say yes. You'd do the same if you were in my position. You told me so this morning. Now, stop behaving like a child and let's go through what we've done this morning and give it a few tweaks so it really hums.'

As it turned out, Cesare appeared a little while later to say that Keith wasn't going to be able to go through the new songs with her until the next day as he had an important Zoom meeting coming up. This gave Steph an idea and she turned to Ethan.

'Why don't I ask Ben if he feels like coming down to the studio to take a look? You never know – we might even be able to persuade him to play something.'

Although Ethan was clearly still miffed at her amazing good fortune at being offered a place on the new album, Steph felt sure he was pragmatic enough to realise that this was too good an opportunity to miss. They both knew that if they could help get the group back together again, this would be a major achievement. Still looking a bit truculent, he agreed, but told her *he* would go and speak to Ben. Steph didn't object. He was her boss, after all. For how much longer of course remained to be seen.

Seeing as she had the studio to herself, she settled down at the keyboard and launched into another of her classical favourites, Beethoven's *Les Adieux* sonata. Much as she enjoyed the modern stuff, her first love was still classical music, and she somehow felt she owed it to her father to take every opportunity to play something he would have appreciated. As so often happened, she lost herself in the music – and it wasn't an easy piece by any means – and she emerged at the end of it feeling refreshed.

Half an hour later she was joined in the studio by Ethan and Ben. Ethan talked him through the equipment, and Ben expressed amazement at the way the technology had progressed in just a decade. While Ben was poking around, Ethan asked Steph to go over to the keyboard and play something so he could demonstrate to Ben the degree to which he could modify and improve the resulting sound. Deciding it was worth taking a chance, she launched into the same solo from Royalty's big hit, 'Getting Back on Top', that she had played for Keith and Johnny. When it came to an end, she waited anxiously for Ben's reaction.

'Wow, Steph, that was magic. It was like hearing Vince all over again.'

There was a catch in Ben's voice, and he looked suddenly serious, so Steph didn't reply. To give him time, she changed to a piece of Mozart, but the seed had been sown. When she finished, Ben was looking more cheerful and he applauded her skill. Taking advantage of his buoyant mood, Ethan came up with a proposal.

'There are some of Keith's guitars over there. Why don't you play something or even join Steph? Having two instruments will give me more scope to demonstrate the range of all this recording gear.'

Ben didn't react for almost a minute and Steph held her breath. At last he walked over and picked up the same acoustic guitar Keith had used earlier and perched on a stool, running his fingers lovingly across the smooth woodwork and stroking the strings. Finally raising his head, he looked across at Ethan.

'Want to hear something new? I wrote it last year. Steph, if you feel like joining in at any point, please do.'

To her delight, he began to play. Unlike so much of Royalty's earlier stuff, this was a gentle ballad, and the lyrics were both personal and moving, clearly autobiographical, as he sang of grief, loss and loneliness. Slowly at first, she joined in with a little bit of backing, and by the end the two of them were beginning to play in unison, and she was even humming along in harmony with him. As the last chords faded, she looked up from the keyboard to see Ben with tears in his eyes, looking shell-shocked, and her immediate thought was that maybe this had been too much, too soon. Neither she nor Ethan said a word, apprehensively waiting for him to react. They had to wait several minutes before he finally rested the guitar against the wall and reached for a tissue in his pocket. He wiped it across his eyes before looking straight at her.

'That was beautiful, Steph. Thank you.' He blew his nose. 'And now I think I need some fresh air.' He walked to the door but stopped on the threshold, turning back towards the two of them. 'Maybe we could do that again?'

'Just say the word.' Ethan's voice was unusually soft and comforting, and Steph was impressed. 'It's been a privilege.'

She waited until the sound of Ben's retreating footsteps on the gravel had disappeared before standing up and joining Ethan at the console.

'Did you manage to get all that?'

'Yes, and it sounded great.' He caught her eye for a moment before surprising her with another unexpected mood swing. 'Keith's not wrong, you know. You're perfect to replace Vince.'

This gentler side was the Ethan she had fallen for in years gone by and she found herself wondering if he really might be able to shed the fast-living persona he had adopted of late and return to being the man she had once loved. She even allowed herself to touch his shoulder for a moment as she answered.

'Thanks, Ethan. That means a lot.'

As if regretting his moment of tenderness, he glanced down at his watch. 'It's almost six. I've got stuff to do. Will you finish up and switch off? I'll see you later.'

–

Just after one o'clock in the morning the storm struck and Steph was awakened by a thunderclap that made her ears ring. This was accompanied almost simultaneously by a flash of lightning that lit up the room. Throwing off the sheet under which she had been sleeping, she got out of bed and padded across to the window just in time to hear the rain start. One moment it wasn't raining, the next moment it was bucketing down. Suddenly, almost as if a dam had breached, a torrential deluge came pouring out of the sky, battering the roof and turning the path outside into a rushing stream in a matter of minutes. Accompanied by further thunderclaps and sheet lightning that spread all the way across the horizon, the storm was intimidating and at the same time spectacular. Along with the rain came a wonderful refreshing breeze that began to dispel the increasingly clammy, humid air that had been building up for hours.

The rain continued to pour down ever harder, and it occurred to Steph that maybe somebody should go and check that the very expensive electrical equipment in the studio wasn't at risk of being flooded. Although she felt sure that Ethan couldn't possibly have slept through such a racket, she doubted that he would be bothered to get up, so she decided that she had better go herself. She pulled on a pair of shorts and a T-shirt and let herself out onto the landing. She tried the light switch out there, but the storm must have knocked out the power. However, the regular flashes of lightning provided more than enough light for her to find her way along to the stairs. As she passed Ethan's door, she wondered whether to tell him where she was going in case he preferred to check on it himself but seeing as she was dressed now – sort of – she carried on down the stairs without him.

A glance out of the front door revealed that the path up to the house had been transformed into a torrent, but it had been designed so as to divert the water away from the building, and the place looked in no danger of being flooded. She opened the door to the studio just to be on the safe side and took a quick look around to see that nothing had been left on that could be damaged by the electrical storm, but all was well. She was just about to go back upstairs again when she heard footsteps and a voice at the foot of the stairs right outside the studio door.

'Oh, hell, I'm going to get soaked.' He was muttering to himself.

Steph froze with her hand on the door handle. The voice unmistakably belonged to Denver. What on earth was he doing here? Had he maybe even come to seek her out? Silently she felt for the bolt on the inside of the studio door and pushed it across while bad-tempered grumbling continued outside for some minutes. She even saw the door handle turn at one point and she blessed the instinct that had made her lock herself in. Finally she heard the front door bang and the sound of running footsteps splashing up the path in the direction of the villa.

She gave it another minute before unbolting the door and peering out into the now empty lobby. Reassured, she stepped out of the studio and pulled the door shut behind her. Checking that the front door was safely closed, she scampered upstairs and into her bedroom, turning the key in the lock behind her. A quick check with the aid of the torch on her phone – even under the bed – confirmed that she was alone and she stretched out on top of the single sheet, her brain swirling.

What had brought Denver down here at one o'clock in the morning? From what he had said about going to get drenched, it was evident that he had been about to leave; he hadn't just arrived. When she had heard his voice, it was because he had come down the stairs and was about to return to the villa. Had he been looking for her in her room and, finding it empty, left again? Alternatively, if he hadn't been coming to see her, then presumably he must

Chapter 9

Next morning the scene that greeted Steph when she looked out of the window was very different from previous days. The rain had stopped, but thick cloud covered the whole sky. As a result, yesterday's clear blue sea was now leaden grey and big waves were crashing against the cliffs at the mouth of the bay, sending spume flying. The smell of ozone reached up to her window and she breathed deeply, relishing the fresher feel to the air. Today she decided not to go swimming, but simply to go for a walk on the beach.

Although the waves down here weren't anything like as big as those out in the gulf, the storm had stirred up the sandy bottom and the water was no longer crystal clear. Clumps of seaweed, pieces of driftwood and assorted bits of detritus littered the shore. Paw prints in the damp sand indicated that the Labrador had been here not too long ago but there was no sign of him now. Looking at the chaotic waves smashing into the cliffs further out, Steph hoped the dog hadn't decided to go for a swim.

Keen to get a better view over the gulf towards La Spezia, she decided to climb one of the cliffs and took a narrow path that led upwards on the opposite side of the bay from Robert's house. She deliberately chose this direction, rather than risk running into him, as she knew full well that she was better off staying well clear of him, in spite of that spark of attraction. The more she thought about it, the more she came round to the realisation that it was probably for the best that he evidently had no interest in her. Let him stick to his bimbos. That way, as she became ever more involved with his father's band, there would be no risk of any sort of emotional entanglement spoiling what promised to be a fantastic chance for her.

Thoughts of Robert reminded her of his big brother, and she questioned, yet again, what Denver might have been doing at the apartment last night. There had been no sign of Ethan when she had come out of her room just now, and she assumed he was catching up on his sleep after the broken night, but had his night been shortened not so much by the storm as by a visit from Denver and, if so, why?

The view from the cliff top was spectacular. She stood there, bracing herself against the buffeting wind, and gazed around. The first thing she saw was Robert's red brick house right on the end of the opposite headland, little more than a hundred metres away across the mouth of the bay. The view from his house had to be similar to the view from where she was standing, and she felt sure it must be a gorgeous place to live on a fine day. On a day like today the noise of the crashing waves no doubt created quite a bit of a disturbance, but that was a small price to pay for a view like this. There was no sign of him or his dog and no sound of his violin – although in this wind it was hard to tell. A glance at her watch told her it was already past eight, so she turned and went back to the guest apartment, stopping off to check that all was still well in the studio first. To her surprise she found Ethan in there, looking frazzled. He glanced up as he heard the door open and rubbed a weary hand across his forehead.

'Hi, Steph. You okay?'

He really didn't look well at all. 'I'm fine, but you look knackered. Is something wrong? Are you sick?'

He shook his head irritably. 'I'm okay. Leave me alone.'

She hesitated before doing as she was told, but she was concerned. It certainly looked as though he hadn't slept well and, once again, she found herself thinking of Denver and his midnight visit. She was still thinking about it when she went up to the villa for breakfast. Today breakfast was set up indoors in the long dining room and she was relieved to see there was no sign of Denver. The only person at the table was Sky and she gave Steph a friendly wave.

'Did you manage to get any sleep? Tom and I hardly slept a wink.'

'Sort of, but that was quite a storm, wasn't it? Is that sort of thing common here?'

'This is the first time I've been here in September. Normally we come in July or August and, although we've had a few storms, we've never had anything as violent as that. Cesare tells me local radio's been saying that a dozen boats lost their moorings, including one of those huge luxury yachts, and the marina looks like a bomb's gone off.'

At that moment, Cesare appeared. 'It's very unusual so early in the autumn. The reason La Spezia's such an important naval base is because it's normally very sheltered. Anyway, Stefania, what can I get you? Your usual, or would you like something more substantial?'

Steph thanked him but just asked for a cappuccino and a croissant and he went off. Returning her attention to Sky, she queried where everybody else was.

'Mum and Dad were up early – sorting stuff out for Friday's party, I think. The others are probably still in bed, trying to catch up on the sleep they lost last night.' She grinned. 'I wonder how Rob got on out there on the cliff top. It must have been scary.'

'Well, his house is still standing. I went down to the sea before coming here and looked across at it. Does he really live there all year round?'

'Yes, all on his own apart from Waldorf.' Steph saw Sky hesitate before continuing. 'Although he does have a number of female visitors. I imagine you've seen the stories in the papers. I'm afraid he's got himself a pretty dodgy reputation.'

Steph nodded. Robert was the son of her current employer after all so she would do well not to dwell on his dubious lifestyle in front of his sister. 'He's a good-looking man and very talented with it. I suppose there are lots of women only too happy to throw themselves at him.'

'Yes, but he's almost thirty now. It's time he started thinking about settling down.'

Steph felt she should play devil's advocate. 'He is younger than you, though, and you're only just getting married now...'

'True, but Tom and I've been living together for almost four years. Look at you: you've got Ethan, haven't you?'

Remembering what she had agreed with him, Steph just nodded vaguely and dodged the question.

They were just finishing breakfast when Willow appeared with a face like thunder. Ignoring Sky's greeting she stomped across to where Steph was sitting and grabbed her shoulder, pulling her round towards her. She lowered her face until it was barely an inch or two from Steph's before hissing at her: 'I know what's going on, you slut! Just you keep your hands off him. Do you hear me?'

For a moment Steph genuinely thought she was about to find herself on the receiving end of a slap, but Willow must have thought better of it. Straightening up, the woman turned away and stormed out of the door, leaving Steph feeling completely bewildered. Opposite her, Sky clearly felt equally bemused by the scene.

'What on earth was that all about? Willow's not the friendliest of people, but I've never seen her like that before.'

'I have no idea.' No sooner had she said it than Steph realised that she might in fact have an idea as to what might have sparked off this incandescent reaction. 'Although… something funny happened last night. I wonder if she put two and two together and got five.'

'What happened?'

Steph briefly outlined how she had heard Denver at the bottom of the stairs outside the studio in the middle of the night and as she spoke, an explanation for Willow's outburst began to emerge in her head. 'Willow must have realised that Denver had been down at the studio where Ethan and I are staying, and she assumed that this meant he was with me.'

'And that's not what was happening?'

'That's not what was happening at all. I heard Denver's voice, but I didn't even see him. Like I say, I was in the studio checking that it wasn't getting flooded. All I can assume is that he was down there to see Ethan for some reason, but why that was in the middle of the night I haven't got a clue.' Her voice tailed off in bewilderment, but Sky leant across the table towards her and gave her a little touch on the back of the hand.

'Steph, does Ethan do drugs?'

Steph looked up sharply. 'What makes you ask that?'

An expression of regret appeared on Sky's face. 'It's no secret that drugs were responsible for killing Vince and almost killing Ben. Dad has a rigid no drugs policy as far as anybody in any of his houses is concerned. I know Den's no stranger to the scene, but even he knows what would happen if Dad ever found out he was doing drugs here, so as far as I know he stays clean when he's with the family. But if somebody else brought drugs into the house he might be tempted again. That's why I ask. Do you think Ethan might have brought drugs with him and supplied them to Den?'

As she listened, Steph had to struggle to avoid revealing the turmoil Sky's question had aroused inside her. Surely Ethan couldn't have been so stupid as to bring drugs over with him. If he'd been caught with them at the airport, she had no illusions that she would probably have ended up being arrested alongside him. Conscious that Sky was waiting for an answer, she opted for dissimulation – for now at least.

'I think alcohol's more his thing. I did have my doubts a few times when we were back in London, but I've never caught him taking anything.' Although strictly true, this was more than a little disingenuous, and she felt ashamed for not being completely honest, but she knew that first she needed to have a serious talk with Ethan. 'I can't believe he would be so stupid as to smuggle anything on the plane and I can't see how he could have got hold of drugs over here. As far as I'm aware, he doesn't know anybody in Italy and he hasn't left the villa. I'd better go and talk to him to find out exactly what was going on last night, before Willow comes back with a carving knife.'

She managed a little smile at Sky. 'I'll let you know what I find out.'

She found Ethan still in the studio, sitting at the console. He had been playing around with the recording Ben had made the previous day and had managed to enhance it even more. In spite of her brewing rage, Steph stopped and listened, genuinely impressed by the result. She waited until the piece had finished before confronting him. She told him about Willow's accusations but stopped short of mentioning what Sky had said about drugs. She wanted to hear what he had to say for himself first. To her surprise, his reaction to the accusation of her hooking up with Denver was to laugh out loud.

'That girl's crazy. Den wouldn't be interested in you.'

Steph decided to ignore the implied slight, but she couldn't miss his use of the abbreviated version of Denver's name. Did this imply greater intimacy?

'Well, I have absolutely no interest in Denver, so I hope you're right. Tell me, if he didn't come down here last night to try and climb into my bed, what was he doing? Presumably he was with you in your room? Feel like letting me know what the two of you were up to?' She knew Ethan well enough to recognise the guilty look that crossed his face, and her heart sank. 'Ethan? What was going on?'

'We were just chatting.' As explanations went, it was hardly inspired. Even he must have realised how weak it sounded as he immediately set about embellishing his story. 'You know... recording stuff. He was telling me how pleased he was with what we did yesterday morning and he wants me to help him prepare a really slick demo for him to hawk around when he's over in the States.' He kept his eyes firmly fixed on the console and refused to look up.

'Just chatting? Ethan, were there drugs involved?'

'Drugs?' His tone was one of hurt pride, but not totally convincing. 'Of course not. I don't do drugs. That would be crazy.'

'Yes, it would and not just because you might get yourself arrested.' She went on to tell him what Sky had said about Keith's inflexible rule and she saw her words hit home. She finished with a warning, 'So if you've brought anything with you, I suggest you flush it down the drain pronto.'

'I didn't bring anything, honest.'

Two things struck her simultaneously. First, she reckoned that this time maybe he *was* telling the truth, and second, she couldn't miss the slight emphasis he put on the pronoun 'I'. Did this mean that if drugs had been involved, they hadn't been brought by him, but by Denver? She wouldn't put it past the man.

She stood there for a full minute before making up her mind. Ethan was no longer her boyfriend and so, technically, what he did in his free time was up to him. Similarly, Denver meant nothing to her so she couldn't care less what he did. What did concern her was the possibility of Keith finding out that Ethan had been dabbling in drugs. If that were to come to Keith's ears, from what Sky had said that would mark the expulsion of Ethan from the villa and the end of this contract. And that, she felt sure, could scupper her chances of accompanying Royalty on their new album, and that would be a crying shame. She gave him her sternest look.

'Two things: please make sure you steer clear of any drugs while you're here, and please ask Denver to tell his lady friend he was with you last night before she decides she's going to assault me with a deadly weapon.'

In return he nodded his head and then dropped his eyes once again. She hoped the message had got through but knew it was time to change the subject. Glancing up at the clock on the wall she saw that it was half past nine already so she adopted a businesslike tone.

'What's the plan for today? When do we get a chance to play Ben's new number to Keith and Johnny?'

Ethan looked up, the relief visible on his face, like a schoolboy who had escaped detention even though he'd misbehaved in class. 'Cesare came down a few minutes ago to say Keith will be delayed but Johnny will be here any minute now.' He let his eyes run over his crumpled clothes as if noticing them for the first time. 'Listen, I need a coffee followed by a shower and a change. Will you look after Johnny for a bit? Play him Ben's new number. See what he thinks of it.'

Steph nodded approvingly and he left. Barely ten minutes later Johnny appeared at the door with his wife alongside him.

'Hi, Steph. Tara wanted to come and take a look. All right with you?'

'Absolutely. Do come in. Ethan and I've got something you might like to hear. See what you think.' She waited until they sat down on a couple of stools and then she pulled up Ben's piece and played it to them, keeping a close eye on the two of them as they listened to it. Tara started beaming within a few seconds of first hearing Ben's voice and the smile never left her face. Beside her, Johnny looked stunned, as if he could hardly believe his ears. When it came to the end, Tara was the first to react.

'Wonderful, amazing, such a beautiful song!' She turned to her husband. 'What did you think, sweetie?'

'I never thought I'd see the day…' Johnny was sounding unusually emotional. 'Ben singing and playing again, it's like a dream. And the words… Did you hear the words: all that pain and grief stuff? I almost burst into tears.' He looked across at Steph. 'I don't know how you did it, but you're a miracle worker. The next step, of course, is to see whether he feels like singing and playing along with us. I tell you this: Keith's going to be over the moon when he hears this.'

Keith was indeed delighted when he heard it a bit later on. His reaction wasn't dissimilar to Johnny's and Steph actually caught sight of what might have been tears in the corners of his eyes. After congratulating her and a freshly showered and changed Ethan on getting Ben to open up like this, Keith came up with a fascinating suggestion.

'Why don't we try and join in? Ethan, would it work if we were to improvise some backing and some harmony? Could you then mix the tracks together and turn this into the first of the born-again Royalty numbers?'

Steph glanced at Ethan and saw the excitement on his face. This was exactly the sort of thing he was so good at. Over the next hours he took Keith and Johnny through the piece over and over again, listening to their interventions, accepting some, rejecting others, suggesting changes until it was time for Steph to add the keyboard track. She had been preparing this in her head and it appeared to be well received. Keith offered little more than a few suggestions and didn't demonstrate any signs of bossiness. Ethan got her to change some of it, but before long he declared himself satisfied.

'This is going to be great. I can feel it.' He looked across at Keith, Johnny and Tara. 'Why don't you guys go off and have a coffee while Steph and I work a bit of magic? Give us an hour or so, all right?'

The result was remarkable and when Keith and Johnny came back and heard it, they looked and sounded ecstatic; so much so that Keith hurried back to the villa and reappeared with Faye and Tara in tow so that they could listen when Ethan played it again. The reaction of the two ladies mirrored that of their husbands.

'That's one of the best things Royalty's ever done.' Faye sounded quite overcome and was openly crying. 'I just love it. It's so, so sad but it's beautiful.'

Her husband stretched a comforting arm around her shoulder. 'Let's just hope Ben feels the same way when he hears it.'

Chapter 10

When Steph emerged from the studio at just after midday, she was delighted to see that the sky was clearing rapidly and much of it was blue again, just punctuated with big fluffy white clouds. She knew she had a bit of time before lunch, so she decided to go for a short walk. First, however, she checked her phone, but there was no email from the hospital. They had told her she should be getting the result of her mammogram any day now and she dreaded the thought of finding out that she might have cancer. Here she was, thinking of her future career, her future life, and it could all be turned on its head if the lump turned out to be malignant. A cold shiver ran down her spine. One of her dad's favourite sayings had been that the most important thing in life was good health – and look what had happened to him.

After the storm the air was a little cooler and amazingly clear, so she did her best to put her fears aside and set off up the path in the direction of Robert's house, determined to see if she could get a view of what lay around the corner of the next promontory. She deliberately avoided going too close to where he lived. She knew nothing could or should happen between the two of them, and she didn't want to run the risk of being tempted – although his apparent indifference towards her made any approach by him unlikely. When she reached the track that linked his house to the main road, she hurried across it into the bushes again. As she followed the winding path, she skirted around the dry-stone wall that marked the boundary of his property. Olive trees within prevented her from getting a clear view of the whole house, but the glimpses she got revealed a lovely ancient building, redolent with character.

She walked along the path through clumps of pines and areas of sun-scorched scrub, climbing slowly until she reached a vantage point on the top of a high cliff from where she could look straight down onto the rocks below and the sea still flecked with foam after the storm. From here she had a fine view over three or four more rocky inlets and then the coast arcing away southwards into Tuscany. She wondered once again if she would have time to take a trip to Florence to see the statue of David or to Pisa to see the Leaning Tower. Ethan had never been keen on history or art but now that they were no longer together, there was no reason she shouldn't jump on a train by herself with a clear conscience.

Of course, there was still a slight question mark in her mind over the future of their relationship. In his gentler moments she still felt some affection for him, but the mood swings that turned him into a bear with a sore head had the opposite effect. Not knowing from one moment to the next what sort of reaction she was going to get from him certainly offered her little incentive to revive the relationship, but the question mark still hung in the air. The other uncertainty was the question of drugs. In spite of his denial, could it be that he had been doing drugs and she hadn't realised? It was an unsettling thought.

There was a treat in store for her when she retraced her steps along the path. Just as she was passing Robert's house his violin struck up with what she immediately recognised as Tchaikovsky's Violin Concerto in D major. As before, the playing was divine and she would happily have hidden herself away behind one of the clumps of bright yellow broom blossoms to listen in silent appreciation, but a glance at her watch told her it was lunchtime. Reluctantly she pressed on down the path onto the beach and up to the villa, the plaintive notes of the violin and thoughts of the man wielding the bow gradually fading behind her.

Lunch was once more served outside on the terrace and today Donatella had laid out a cold buffet around a whole big fish on a platter, cooked and de-boned and then covered with scores of thin slices of cucumber to make it look like scales. She gave the name of the white-fleshed fish in Italian, but Steph had no idea of the translation into English. Irrespective of its name, the taste was exceptional. Accompanied by a variety of mixed salads, one of them a combination of tiny boiled potatoes, hardboiled eggs, black olives and spicy prawns in homemade mayonnaise, it was a real feast. Although she had been trying to avoid drinking wine at lunchtime, Steph allowed herself a glass of the excellent local white and, in spite of her fractious relationship with Ethan, Willow's dire threats, and the trepidation about the scan results, she felt herself relaxing in the warm Italian sunshine. Whether this new-found peace had anything to do with the violin music she had just heard was something she chose not to debate.

She helped herself to a plate of food and took a seat at a table with Sky and Tom, suitably distanced from Willow who was deep in conversation with Denver at the other end of the terrace. As Steph started eating, she saw Ethan approach Denver's table and sit down with them. Hopefully over the course of the meal he and Denver would be able to explain to Willow what had taken place last night and reassure her that Steph herself had not been involved. Steph certainly hoped so. She had no desire to find herself on the receiving end of another violent verbal attack or worse. Willow might be small, but Steph didn't want to find out how well she could handle herself in a fight.

'So, Steph, how did this morning's recording session go?'

Sky's voice roused her from her thoughts. Taking a quick look around to check that Ben and Lottie weren't within earshot, she gave them a big smile. 'It went better than any of us hoped.' She gave them a quick summary of how Keith and Johnny had taken Ben's new number and added their own tracks to the mix. 'It sounds amazing: vintage Royalty but with a poignant, emotional feel. I was almost in tears.'

'Has Ben heard what they've done to it yet?' Sky also cast a wary eye towards the neighbouring table.

'Nope. Your dad's trying to decide when the best time to spring it on him is going to be.'

'Just make sure you take your time with Ben. He's still very fragile.' It was so unusual to hear normally taciturn Tom speak that Steph was momentarily stumped.

'You know him well?'

'Not Ben himself, but I've met a lot of people with similar problems.'

Seeing the uncertainty on Steph's face, Sky added a few words of explanation. 'Tom's a psychotherapist. He spends his life listening to people's problems.'

Steph realised she had been guilty of underestimating Tom. She had to some extent dismissed him as a beach bum with his hippy clothes, occasional laconic comments and his laid-back approach to life. Never judge a book by its cover had been another one of her dad's favourite English sayings and this proved, yet again, how right he had been. She gave Tom a smile.

'I would imagine there are more than enough people with problems in the world today to keep you busy.'

He nodded. 'You're not wrong. With so many bad things happening, it's getting harder and harder for people to cope.'

A thought occurred to Steph, and she threw out the question to both of them. 'The other day, after Denver's big blow-up, Faye said he'd been under a lot of pressure. Do you know what that's all about? Denver doesn't look particularly stressed.'

Sky answered first. 'It's his career. I don't think it's working out as well as he's been hoping. I get the feeling he resents not being as successful as Dad.'

'We can't all become living legends.' Steph glanced along the terrace to where Denver was still in conversation with Ethan and Willow. 'But Denver told me he's got a season at Caesar's Palace coming up. That sounds pretty good.'

'For most people, yes, definitely, but Denver doesn't think of himself as most people.'

Tom took over from Sky. 'When you're the son of a megastar it's almost inevitable that you measure yourself against them and, like you say, Steph, we can't all be living legends.'

Sky was quick to retort. 'Well, he's my father too, and I don't feel pressured.'

'Ah, sweetie, that's because you had the good sense to marry a shrink. We have our uses.'

Any further discussion was interrupted by the arrival of Willow. The expression on her face wasn't exactly contrite, but it was less aggressive than before. 'I need to speak to you, Steph.'

Steph braced herself and nodded. 'Okay...'

Willow wasted no time. 'Listen, Den tells me I need to apologise for what I said earlier. I must have got the wrong idea about what was going on. Ethan and Den have explained what was happening and told me that you had nothing to do with it.'

Steph took a closer look at her. In spite of her words, Willow looked far from remorseful, and Steph couldn't miss the fact that she hadn't actually apologised; just said she should. Still, anything was better than assault with a deadly weapon, so Steph decided to be magnanimous.

'I'm glad that's been cleared up. I must admit I've been really taken aback by your attitude, not just this morning, but ever since I arrived. Just let me make myself totally clear: I have absolutely no interest in your boyfriend and if he were to try anything with me, I would slap him so hard they'd hear it over on the other side of the bay. Understood?'

Willow pursed her lips 'If you say so.' As apologies went, this was grudging, to say the least, and Steph had to struggle to avoid snapping at her.

'I do say so, and you can tell your boyfriend that from me if you like.' Seeing as she had Willow's attention, she decided to do a bit of digging. 'Tell me, just what did Denver give as a reason for deciding to visit my boyfriend in the middle of the night? Are they planning a robbery or something?'

Willow gave a helpless shrug of the shoulders. 'He didn't say much. He just said he had stuff to discuss with Ethan, about his music I think.'

That squared with what Ethan had said, but Steph still smelt a rat. After all, why should Denver choose the middle of the night and the middle of a storm to visit his record producer? As an alibi it was decidedly shaky, but for now she left her suspicions unvoiced.

'Anyway, as long as we're clear. Me and your boyfriend: not going to happen.'

For a moment it looked as though Willow might be about to retort but, instead, she just nodded again, turned and walked away.

'Not exactly gracious in defeat.' Sky sounded as sceptical as Steph felt. 'I wouldn't call that a heartfelt apology, would you?'

Steph shrugged. 'Probably the best I could hope for. At least it would appear that the message is gradually getting through to Willow that I'm not trying to snaffle her man from her. I'd still like to know what was going on last night, though. I'm going to have to speak to Ethan.'

'What *is* the situation between you and Ethan, if you don't mind me asking?' Sky glanced along the terrace to the table where Ethan and Denver were still talking. 'Are you two together?'

'We were, but now we aren't.' Steph decided she owed them the truth, and as she spoke, she realised that she meant what she said. All of these suspicions about drugs and secret meetings coupled with his unpredictable mood swings had finally made her realise that her future, at least at a non-professional level, wasn't going to include Ethan. 'It's been brewing for some time but it's all over now, and I'm glad I've made the decision.'

At the end of the meal, Keith came over to ask if Steph could spare a bit of time to go through the new material he had written, so that she would be better able to join in with the next recording session. As a result, she spent an enjoyable hour and a half in the studio with him, playing around with different arrangements until she was reasonably familiar with three or four of the numbers for the new album. The fact that there was no written music to work from made things tricky, but she managed and found him far easier to work with than she had feared. From time to time she almost had to pinch herself that here she was not only in the presence of a rock god but actually jamming with him and about to appear on his new album with him – assuming it went ahead. Teenage Steph would have exploded with joy if she could have seen into the future.

Around mid-afternoon Ethan appeared, followed a few minutes later by Johnny, and it developed into a full-on recording session. By five o'clock they had another two new songs in the can, and the album was taking shape. There was just one thing – or person – missing and Johnny was the first to voice the problem.

'If only we could get Ben involved. We've got some really good stuff here.' He looked across at Keith. 'When do you think we should play him the mix of his new number with our backing?'

Keith shrugged helplessly. 'I've been trying to work that out. The last thing I want is to scare him off. Tomorrow's our anniversary so if you agree, maybe let's wait until after that.'

And the anniversary party would see Denver stuck on a boat all day with his half-brother. That promised to be interesting.

Chapter 11

The Bailey's anniversary cruise was certainly interesting.

On Friday morning they were all ferried out from the beach to the specially chartered yacht in a beautiful, highly varnished motor launch. As she waited on the sand for her turn, Steph was delighted to discover that the Labrador would also be coming. He arrived on the beach on the end of a lead held by his master, who was evidently taking no chances that the dog might decide to leap into the sea and then come and shake himself all over everybody. Steph wasn't taking any chances either. She was wearing one of her new tops and her new shorts over her bikini, but she had brought a towel and a complete change of clothes with her in a little backpack just in case. She also had a bottle of sun cream in her bag as it was once again a spectacular day without a cloud in the sky.

The trip out to the motor yacht took barely a couple of minutes and the yacht itself was incredible. It was a huge vessel with two decks, white-uniformed staff and a vast lounge – or stateroom as it was called – that was as luxurious as the very best hotel Steph had ever visited. She was awestruck to discover that the yacht had already picked up a number of special guests, among them one whose name came straight out of the Rock 'n' roll Hall of Fame. This was Cody Havergill, legendary bad boy of the rock world, who had allegedly trashed more hotel rooms than Steph had had hot dinners. She hadn't seen or heard of him for some years and seeing him now came as quite a shock.

He was about the same age as Keith, somewhere around sixty, but unlike Keith he hadn't aged well. He now looked as though he was more likely to fall asleep in a chair by the fire than cause mayhem. Along with him was a chunky bodyguard bizarrely wearing a dark suit in spite of the blazing sunshine. In the course of the day the bodyguard and Cody between them ate more than the rest of the group put together. Cody also did his best to drink the boat dry and was barely able to stand by the end.

Steph would desperately have liked to take a whole host of photos and send them to her mum, but she and Ethan had been warned in advance that, understandably, today was a no photo event.

She sipped her champagne and wondered if Ethan would be able to control himself and stay sober. The previous night he had once again done his best to drink himself into a stupor and she had had to warn him that Keith was looking as though he was beginning to get fed up with this behaviour. As a result, Ethan had left the dinner table early muttering that he was going to bed, although when Steph got back to the guest apartment it had been to find him in the studio, sprawled across the recording console, passed out. She had left him there and made sure she locked her bedroom door before going to bed.

When all the guests were on board, the yacht set off across the bay. There was virtually no wind, just a very pleasant breeze, and the sea was as calm as a millpond. This suited Steph down to the ground as she had never been a good sailor. She stood outside on the upper observation deck for a while, admiring the view and soaking up the sun. Her pale English legs and arms had begun to collect a bit of colour, and it was wonderful to feel the fresh sea breeze on her skin. She was joined up there by Sky who told her that she and Tom would be leaving in two days' time. When Steph expressed disappointment, Sky explained.

'We've been here for almost a month now and we both need to get back to work.' She glanced around to check that they weren't being overheard. 'And, to be honest, I can't wait to get away from Den and that girl. Have you seen what she's wearing today? Fancy turning up for a cruise and a picnic in high heels! The crewman made her take them off so as not to damage the teak deck and now she looks tiny, doesn't she? She also looks livid. Did you hear Denver complaining? Mind you, Denver's always complaining about something.'

Steph felt it was wiser not to get dragged into slagging off the other guests or family members, so she just nodded.

As they stood there, looking over towards the opposite shore of the gulf that was drawing nearer, they both witnessed a scene on the deck below them. Most of the other guests had collected down there, drinking and chatting, and Denver was conspicuous as he mingled with the celebrities, clearly loving every minute of it. At one point, his mingling brought him to where his half-brother was standing making sure his dog didn't try to help himself to the contents of a silver salver of nibbles. As Denver spotted Robert a smile appeared on his face, but it wasn't a friendly fraternal smile.

'Hi, Rob, I wondered if you and your mutt would show up. How's life working out for you with your violin?

I suppose classical music doesn't pay like real music, does it?'

'I'm doing fine, thanks.' The expression on Robert's face was hard to read. It was a mixture of discomfort, dislike and apprehension. 'How're things with you?'

'Really good. I have a place in Beverly Hills now. A bit different from that shack where you live.'

'Don't start, Den. It's not a shack. It's a great house.'

'Don't start what?'

'Your usual snide remarks. Can't you just try and be a nice person for once?'

'I am a nice person with people I like.' The disdain in Denver's voice was clear to hear.

Robert's tone hardened. 'Well, sod off and talk to somebody else, will you? And remember it's Mum and Dad's anniversary, so try not to spoil it.'

'Why don't you just jump overboard and make us all happy.'

Robert stared hard at his brother for a few seconds and the tension in the air was palpable even from high above. Finally, he glanced down at the dog. 'Come on, Waldorf. Let's go and get a change of air.'

'No, you stay here. I'm off.' With a dismissive wave of the hand, Denver turned away and left.

Steph looked across at Sky in disbelief. 'So much for brotherly love…' She kept her voice low although Robert had moved across to the far side of the deck and was engaged in conversation with an attractive dark-haired woman.

'It's not pretty, is it?'

'How sad to see them fighting. Have they always been like this?'

123

'Den has. For years Rob just meekly took it, but he's finally realised that the only way to treat a bully is to stand up to him.' After another covert glance in all directions, she continued. 'It's such a shame, but there's no doubt it's Den's fault. He's always treated his little brother like dirt.'

Steph looked back down at the tall, handsome man with his equally handsome dog beside him. 'Not such a *little* brother now.'

'I know. I sometimes think Den deliberately tries to wind Rob up in the hope that he'll lash out. A black eye would be a small price to pay for seeing his brother fall out of favour with Mum and Dad.'

'Your mum said you know how to deal with Denver. Why didn't you teach Robert?'

Sky shrugged helplessly. 'I'm afraid it's too late for that. The damage has been done. Still, with Den living in the US now, Rob's much happier. He was with us every day last month and he was looking and sounding really relaxed.'

'So does this mean you got to meet some of his lady friends?' This was a bit personal, but Sky didn't seem to mind.

'Not one. He keeps them very much at arm's length. He certainly didn't bring anybody up to the villa.'

'A bit tough on his girlfriends.'

'I'm not so sure. I take all the newspaper stories with a pinch of salt. I think there are some women who prey on men like him for the publicity it provides. Don't get me wrong, he's no angel, but I think he's more sinned against than sinning.'

The yacht passed through the narrow straits between the wooded slopes of the island of Palmaria and the mainland, and rounded a rocky headland to reveal Portovenere, which was, as Cesare had indicated, quite stunning. As the name implied, it was a little port with a harbour full of moored boats, but it was the backdrop of houses that really made it stand out. The whole harbour area was lined with traditional Italian town houses, all joined together, some even four or five storeys high, all with dark green shutters but each house painted a different colour ranging from light cream through a whole palette of oranges, blues, greens and even bright red. On the hillside above the town was an ancient fortress and the overall impression was charming. The trouble was that, even from out here, they could see that the place was heaving with people. For that reason, their yacht with its celebrities on board didn't put into port but swung around and returned to the island.

They anchored just off the far side of the island and the launch ferried them ashore to a little sandy beach between rocky outcrops. Sky and Tom wasted no time in stripping to their swimming things and plunging into the crystal-clear water in the company of the Labrador and his master. Steph followed them and soon found herself floating about surrounded by most of the others. Unfortunately, she also found herself a bit too close for comfort to Denver. He came up behind her without her seeing him and the first she knew of his proximity was a voice at her ear.

'Has anybody told you how good you look in a bikini?'

She swung round so she was facing him and paddled backwards to a safe distance just in case.

'That's a very personal remark to make to one of your father's employees.'

'Employee? The way they're treating you anybody would think you were part of the family.'

'Well, I'm not, even if your mum and dad and your sister have been very kind.'

His face hardened. 'Faye's not my mum.'

'Whatever, but they've all been very welcoming.'

'Well, I'm just being welcoming as well, and all I was saying is that you look good.'

He wasn't making any attempt to draw nearer so she gave him the benefit of the doubt. After all, she couldn't really accuse him of anything too improper. 'Well, thank you for the compliment.' An idea came to her. 'But Ethan doesn't like it when other men pay me compliments, so I'd be grateful if you stopped.'

For a moment she felt she could see him weighing up how he might fare in a confrontation with Ethan, who was a tall, strong man, before he retreated with dignity.

'Okay, enough said. Enjoy the rest of the day.'

Steph heaved a sigh of relief. It appeared that Ethan hadn't told him they were now no longer together. This should continue to provide a welcome line of defence.

Denver turned away and swam off and that would probably have been the last of it except for the fact that Steph suddenly felt herself being watched. Looking past the retreating head and shoulders of Denver, her eyes alighted on Willow who was standing in the shallows staring hard at her and the expression on her face was unequivocal. Had they been two dogs, Willow would have bared her fangs to reinforce her territorial message. Steph, relieved that there were twenty metres of water separating them, gave her a cheery wave and turned away. She hoped that Denver had now got the message that she wasn't interested, but it appeared that the same couldn't be said for his girlfriend.

Steph decided to stay in the water for a while longer in the hope that Willow would lose interest, so she bobbed around for several minutes until she saw Denver reach the beach where Willow made a proprietorial grab for him and led him away. Steph then started to swim lazily back in the direction of the shore, and she soon found she had company in the shape of a big black dog.

'*Ciao, bello*. Enjoying your swim?'

The dog then did his best to climb onto her shoulders and almost drowned her in the process. She was rescued from his affectionate advances by his master.

'*Waldorf, vieni qui!* He hasn't scratched you, has he?'

Steph brushed her hair out of her eyes and gave him a smile. '*Ciao*, Robert, I'm fine, thanks.'

She was mildly surprised to see him swim closer to her and as the two of them floated about, they chatted, while the dog kept coming over to nudge her with his nose. Although barely more than monosyllabic at first, Robert eventually began to loosen up to some extent. In true British fashion they started by talking about the weather but then moved on to his career. Slightly reluctantly he told her it was going well, and that he was performing at an outdoor concert near Florence in a couple of days' time. As he began to relax in her company and she in his, he asked about her career and when she told him about the offer she had received from his father to play along with them on the new album, he sounded genuinely pleased for her.

Although all she could see of him was his head and his bare shoulders, she couldn't ignore the feeling of attraction he aroused in her. There was a hint of a smile on his face today and for the first time she found herself looking into his bright blue eyes at close range. There was no getting away from the fact that he was very appealing, but she warned herself not to do anything silly. Men like him needed a WARNING sign on their foreheads. Besides, as she recovered from the demise of her own relationship with Ethan, the last thing she needed was to get involved with another man, particularly when he was the son of the man who could materially advance or destroy her career, and a womaniser to boot. No, it was much safer to avoid Robert, although her head and her heart weren't necessarily in complete agreement over this.

Back at the beach Cesare and Donatella, assisted by members of the yacht's crew, had set up trestle tables and heaped them with food until there was a vast selection of cold dishes to choose from. There were bottles of wine and beer in ice buckets along with soft drinks on one table and another laden with a mouth-watering choice of desserts. Gradually they all helped themselves and took their plates to convenient spots to eat their lunch. Steph toyed with the idea of slipping off somewhere to change out of her wet bikini first, but almost everybody else was just in swimming gear – apart from Cody Havergill's bodyguard who was looking decidedly uncomfortable in his suit – so she decided to let the sun dry her, and on a spectacular day like today she knew that wouldn't take long.

She looked around and saw Robert and his faithful dog sitting with the dark-haired woman from the yacht. Steph had no intention of interfering with him and what might prove to be his latest conquest, so she looked over to where Keith and Faye were with Sky and Tom, chatting to Cody Havergill, but decided against intruding on them. Rather than go and sit somewhere on her own and maybe risk another approach from Denver or assault by Willow, who was now stripped to a bikini that looked as if it had been designed to fit Barbie, she went over to a long flat slab of rock where Ben and Lottie were sitting. He was looking relaxed and happy, and, beside him, Lottie was still wearing the broad smile on her face that had been there almost since day one. They welcomed her and as they chatted, Steph gradually brought the subject around to music, but stayed studiously away from Ben's music and the prospect of him returning to the band.

'I've just been talking to Robert. He tells me he's doing a concert in a Roman amphitheatre near Florence on Sunday afternoon. I was wondering about maybe going to hear him play.'

Lottie looked up with interest. 'That sounds like a super idea.' She turned to her husband. 'Benny, how would you feel about a bit of classical music for a change?'

'I'd love that. Rob plays so beautifully, and I like the idea of a performance in a Roman amphitheatre – reminds me of when we did that gig at the Arena di Verona all those years ago.' For a fraction of a second Lottie caught Steph's eye and winked. Clearly, she viewed her husband talking about the band as progress. 'Why don't we have a word with Keith and see if Cesare might be able to take us in the minibus?' His wife looked delighted to hear him sound so positive.

At that moment, Steph's phone bleeped, and her heart skipped a beat when she saw that it was an email from the hospital in England. She opened it and as she read through the letter a cold numb feeling descended on her. It was couched in formal medical terms, but the upshot was that an appointment had been made for her the following Tuesday at the hospital for a biopsy. The letter indicated that this was a routine investigation to exclude anything serious. She had limited experience of mammograms, but she wondered if this really was as routine as it sounded. Presumably they had spotted something that didn't look right.

'What is it, Steph? Bad news?' Lottie must have seen from Steph's face that something was wrong. She reached over and caught hold of her hand and gave it a squeeze. 'Can I help?'

Steph slipped her phone back in her pocket and looked up, debating what to say. In the end the sympathetic expression on Lottie's face convinced her to reveal everything, including her fears about the significance of the biopsy. Lottie's grip on her hand tightened.

'It'll be all right, you'll see. It's just that they want to be sure. I had a biopsy on a suspicious lump ten years back. I was terribly worried for a few days, but it all came back negative and I'm sure it'll be the same for you.'

Steph gave her a grateful smile. 'Thanks, Lottie, that's really helpful.'

Ben leant over towards her and added a bit more reassurance. 'If you knew the number of medical procedures I've had over the years, you'd realise that a little thing like a biopsy's nothing. It's good that they're being thorough, but try not to worry.'

A bit later, after Cesare and Donatella had cleared away all the rubbish, the launch ferried everybody back to the yacht again. By this time even the Labrador had completely dried out in the sunshine and Steph herself was able to simply slip her clothes back on over her bikini without having to hop on the spot somewhere to get changed under a towel. On the way back towards La Spezia, Keith made a little speech, thanking Faye for thirty years of devotion and thanking his three children for their love. Steph couldn't help glancing across at Denver's face when his father said this, but there was nothing in his expression that reflected the anger he had demonstrated the other day. Whatever his father had said to him, it appeared to have cooled his temper. Of course, maybe Keith had given him a car...

They docked briefly at La Spezia where the celebrities and their entourages all left, stepping straight into a fleet of ostentatious, if anonymous, limousines with tinted windows. As Cody was helped unsteadily down the gangway by his bodyguard, he waved kisses and shouted fulsome thanks and farewells. Steph was surprised and impressed to see him still standing after everything he had drunk but, of course if the tabloids were right, he had had a lot of practice. Down on the main deck, Ethan was looking very pleased with himself. Being able to make contact with a rock legend like Cody was all he had ever wanted, and no doubt today had provided him with some excellent leads which wouldn't do his business any harm at all. Whether Steph would still be involved with his business when that time came, was another matter entirely.

She took advantage of a quiet moment on the way back to the villa to inform Ethan she had to go back to the UK for a medical appointment on Tuesday, bracing herself for disinterest or even an annoyed outburst, but was pleasantly surprised to find him most supportive when she told him what was going on.

'You should have mentioned it before, Steph. I didn't realise you were having problems. How long do you think you'll be away?'

'The appointment's on Tuesday at eleven thirty, so if I fly home last thing on Monday I can get a flight back to Pisa on Tuesday late afternoon or evening so I should only miss one day's work. I've just been checking flight times and it looks like there are still seats.'

'Then go ahead and book. I'm sure Cesare will give you a lift to the station, if not to the airport itself.'

Back at the villa that evening, on Keith's instructions Cesare and Donatella organised another barbecue for the family. Steph protested that she and Ethan should duck out and give them some privacy, although she could almost hear Ethan grinding his teeth as she spoke, but Faye and Keith insisted they join them. Interestingly, tonight Robert was also part of the group – minus the dark-haired woman who had disembarked at La Spezia – although Steph could see him making sure he steered clear of his big brother. In fact, when they all sat down around the big table on the terrace, she saw Robert wait until Denver and Willow had taken their seats before placing himself at the opposite end of the table, where Steph also happened to be sitting chatting to Sky.

As he sat down she felt a warm body rub against her thigh and she looked down to see two big eyes reflecting eerily green in the candlelight as they gazed up at her.

'*Ciao*, Waldorf. Had a good day?' In return she got a nudge from a cold wet nose and a reply from his master.

'He's had a great day. I shudder to think how much he's had to eat. I saw Cody's bodyguard feeding him stuff all day long. Whatever you do, don't let him persuade you to give him any more or he'll explode. What about you? Enjoy yourself?'

Steph was surprised to hear him sounding relatively relaxed. She was also mildly surprised to find that he had chosen to sit near her, although she knew it was simply because he was trying to get as far away from his brother as possible. It actually worked out quite well that he was sitting alongside her, rather than opposite her; that way she didn't have to run the gauntlet of getting dragged in by those magnetic eyes of his. She concentrated her attention on the table in front of her as she replied. 'Definitely. This is a beautiful part of the world. I can see why you decided to put down roots here. You live up on the headland, don't you?'

'Yes. The year after Dad got this place I saw it up for sale, so I bought it. You'll never guess who used to live there.'

'Somebody famous? Byron or Shelley, maybe?'

He shook his head. 'Somebody closer to my heart – Paganini himself.'

'Wow, arguably the most famous violin player of all time! I can see why it appealed to you.'

'I felt an immediate connection with the place. Plus, it's in an amazing position.'

'It certainly is. I was up on the opposite headland the day after the storm, and I couldn't help thinking what a wonderful view you must have from your house. Did the place need much work?'

'It needed a *lot* of work. I did quite a bit of it myself. I enjoy getting my hands dirty.'

Steph was surprised and impressed: somehow she had assumed that his mega-rich father was the owner of the house or that he had gifted it to his son, and so, the idea of a world-famous musician getting involved in a bit of DIY was unexpected. Clearly Robert was trying to make it on his own two feet.

'What happens to Waldorf when you go off to play all over the world? You don't take him with you, surely.' Or did one of his many women move in for the duration? The answer was closer to home.

'No, I leave him with Cesare and Donatella. It's so convenient having them living close by.'

'It must be nice to be near your family.' She saw him glance towards the other end of the table, but he made no comment.

They chatted over dinner, which was a magnificent mixed grill comprising everything from Donatella's fabulous homemade burgers to lamb chops, coils of spicy sausage and huge chunks of steak accompanied by a mountain of fries and sumptuous mixed salads. For those who weren't fans of so much meat, there were slices of aubergine, pecorino cheese and courgettes, all grilled on the barbecue as well. Steph tried some of each and found them delicious.

By the end of the meal her opinion of Robert had risen. In spite of his lurid reputation there was no denying that he was bright as well as good-looking. He also sounded remarkably grounded and free from the pretentious attitude of his older brother. Nevertheless, she reminded herself, he was best avoided, not that there was any reason to believe that he had any great interest in her anyway. He did at least appear more communicative now that they were getting to know each other, but she couldn't sense anything more than friendly interest.

She had an unexpectedly pleasant evening chatting to him on one side of her, and to Sky on the other, and when eleven o'clock arrived she was feeling very relaxed. When the party broke up, she thanked Keith and Faye for the invitation and thanked her dinner companions for their company. It had been a good day. She wandered back down to her room and collapsed into bed. After all the fresh air she should have dropped straight off to sleep, but the thought of the email she had received from the hospital dispelled the memory of what had been an exciting day and replaced it with a cold nagging fear deep down inside.

Chapter 12

Robert's concert on Sunday turned into a group outing for the family. Not all the family, as Denver and Willow abstained, as did Ethan, which came as no surprise to Steph. Classical music, along with history and art, had never been among his interests. Cesare drove all three band members and their wives to Florence in the minibus, along with Tom and Sky who were going to get on a train to Milan to catch their flight back to Manchester. Because Steph was unsure how much longer she would be staying in Italy, she travelled to Florence by train early that morning so that she could take a quick look at the sights. Cesare arranged that he would pick her up from Florence main station at two o'clock when he came to drop Sky and Tom off in time for the Milan train. Cesare would then take the remainder of them to the concert in Fiesole on the outskirts of the city.

Florence was heaving with people when Steph emerged from the station. It was another beautiful September day and crowds of tourists filled the streets, admiring and photographing the wonders of one of the most beautiful cities in the world. Making her way past Renaissance palazzi, medieval churches and designer shops, and heading towards the duomo, she reflected on Sky's final words to her just before she had set off. They had hugged goodbye and Steph had wished her all the best for her wedding day, knowing she would miss her. They had formed a close bond in a short space of time, but it was what Sky had said that was still resonating inside her head.

'Take good care of Rob. I can see that he likes you, and I think the two of you could be good together.'

Steph had been flabbergasted, but she felt she had to express her reservations. 'I can't say I've noticed any great attraction on his part, but I'll be quite honest, Sky, I'm not sure he's the kind of man I want to get mixed up with. I'm sorry if that sounds rude and I take your point that it takes two to tango, but the fact remains that he has got a bit of a reputation.'

'I know what you mean – the *playboy virtuoso* and all that – but like I said before, deep down he's a good guy, and I'm not just saying that because he's my brother. He's been a bit of a lost soul for the past few years, but he's changing, I can feel it. There's something about the way he looks at you that tells me this time it's different.'

As Steph squeezed between a group of Chinese tourists and a troop of Boy Scouts who sounded as though they were from somewhere in Eastern Europe, the thought that Robert might like her was still uppermost in her head. She was amazed that Sky thought there might be anything there. Steph wasn't the most experienced of people in matters of the heart, but she felt sure she could read greater affection in the eyes of his Labrador than in those of the man himself. Could his sister be right?

And if she was, so what?

Even if he was somehow a changed man as his sister had indicated, his dubious reputation with women, the disparity between their backgrounds and the itinerant life-style imposed on him by his career would make it hard to sustain a relationship. Add to that the uncertainty of her future from a professional point of view, and it all became terribly complicated. And of course, there was also the lurking fear of a cancer diagnosis that made her future even more uncertain, but she made a valiant effort to keep that submerged for now. As her mum had told her when she had phoned to pass on the news about Tuesday's biopsy, there was no point in worrying about something over which she had no control.

Easier said than done.

She stopped as she reached the Piazza del Duomo and stood there, eyes ranging over the ornate marble façade of the cathedral with its pillars, arches, statues and decorative lines of different coloured marble, but barely registering the beauty of the scene. She had no idea whether Sky might be right and her brother really did like her, but it made no difference. Nothing could or should happen between them and that was that. Whether he was still a womaniser or not, he had his life and she had hers. And by keeping him at arm's length she would save herself the heartache of ultimate separation.

She didn't have time to visit the interior of the duomo, so she moved on through the busy streets to Piazza della Signoria and fought her way close enough to the massive statue of David to take a few photos. From there she walked on further weaving with difficulty through the crowds to the Ponte Vecchio, where she bought a little necklace for her mum. By this time it was already lunch-time, and she was getting peckish. She was relieved to find a table outside a *gelateria* where she could sit under a parasol and enjoy a bowl of strawberry, peach and white chocolate ice cream. She sent a few photos to her mother and before long it was time to set off for the station to meet Cesare.

She was still thinking about the biopsy and Robert as she waited by the station at two o'clock. Cesare arrived barely a few minutes late to offload Sky and Tom so they could catch their train and Steph took their place in the minibus. Sky added further coals to the fire by whispering in Steph's ear as they hugged one last time, 'You and Rob: I can see it happening. You've got my phone number. Please keep me posted.'

Fiesole lies on a hill, just a handful of kilometres outside Florence. As the car climbed the winding road out of the city, Cesare told them to look back behind them, and the views over Florence were indeed stunning with its mass of red roofs punctuated by spires, towers and the unmistakable cupola of the duomo standing out above all else. When they got to Fiesole, they found it was a charming little town with an open-air market in the main square selling all sorts of lovely looking handcrafted objects. The Roman amphitheatre was impressive, far bigger than Steph had been expecting. Surrounded by beautifully kept grounds and facing away from Florence into the Tuscan countryside, it had been remarkably well preserved, and they found themselves sitting on the two-thousand-year-old stone seats among a thousand other people.

Despite the concert being sold out, Rob had got them seats right in the middle near the front. They sat looking directly onto the stage and, beyond that, there were just olive groves and the Tuscan hills. The seats were completely exposed to the afternoon sun and Steph was glad she had heeded Cesare's advice to bring sun cream. Beside her, the three surviving members of Royalty wore baseball caps and the inevitable dark glasses, and nobody appeared to recognise them or, if they did, they were too polite to say anything. As a souvenir, Steph bought herself a T-shirt with Robert's face on it, advertising the concert. At least she would have something to remember him by when she returned to England.

The concert featured Robert – Rob Sinclair as he appeared on the programme – accompanied by the Florence Chamber Orchestra, and they started with the same Tchaikovsky violin concerto that Steph had heard him practising back on the coast. He was wearing a formal dark tuxedo, complete with bow tie, and he looked good, although he must have been boiling, even though the stage was shaded by a canopy. The combination of the historic setting, the spectacular views, the wonderful weather and his faultless playing resulted in an unforgettable experience. When the concert finished after numerous encores, and the audience began to leave the arena, Steph felt sure people must have found it a perfect and moving experience. She certainly had.

She and the others went down to the front where their backstage passes allowed them through to the restricted area where they found Robert minus his jacket and tie, mopping his face with a towel. His mother went across to give him a hug.

'Robbie, darling, that was simply lovely. You played perfectly.'

He gave her a grin. 'Thanks, I thought it went pretty well. Pity about that aircraft partway through the second movement, but that's the trouble with playing outdoors.' When his eyes landed on Steph he gave her a little smile and a wave before returning to drying himself off. When his face emerged from the towel, he was approached by an enthusiastic admirer who addressed him in Italian and he slipped seamlessly into the language.

A waiter came around with glasses of Prosecco and soft drinks, but after all the sun this afternoon Steph helped herself to a big glass of water and swallowed half of it in one go. Over the next half hour, she made sure to give Robert space and she chatted to Cesare, who was effusive in his praise for the performance. At last Keith waved to Cesare and turned to Robert.

'Rob, we're off back to the villa. Very well done again. You can't imagine how proud we are of you.'

Robert gave him a broad smile in return, hugged his mother and was just waving goodbye to them all when he sneezed. It was only as he pulled out a tissue and blew his nose that he suddenly gave a heartfelt groan and crouched down, running his hands over the grass at his feet. Steph was the last of the group and she turned back to offer help.

'What's happened? Have you dropped something?'

He glanced up. 'My damn contact lens. The left one's been uncomfortable all day and it must have come out when I sneezed. Now I've gone and lost it.'

Steph crouched down alongside him and started running her fingers across the grass as well. 'What does it feel like?' She had no experience of contacts. 'Is it glass? Will it be expensive to replace?'

'That's not the problem. They're daily disposable lenses made of plastic, so I just throw them away every night. But stupidly I didn't think to bring spares, and the glasses I keep in the car are being fixed. The trouble is that I'm supposed to be driving home later on.'

By this time Faye had also noticed that something was wrong, and she and the others came hurrying back. Together they searched, but they searched in vain. A tiny transparent piece of plastic on a lawn was like the proverbial needle in a haystack. Finally they gave up. By this time Keith had realised the problem that Robert now faced.

'It's not safe for you to drive, so why don't you leave the car here and come back in the van with us? There's bags of space. You can pick the car up in the morning.'

Robert shook his head. 'It's not as straightforward as that, I'm afraid. There's a municipal reception at Fiesole town hall coming up shortly and I really have to be there. I can't keep you guys waiting around until eight o'clock or later. You wouldn't get home until late.'

It was then that Faye came up with a suggestion. On the face of it, it seemed very sensible, but Steph spent the rest of the evening wondering whether Sky might have sown the seed of the idea in her mother's head. 'Steph, do you drive? Would you maybe be able to hang on here with Rob and then drive him home? I've never really got used to driving on the wrong side of the road and Keith and the rest of us have been drinking wine, and I'm sure you know how hot the Italian police are on drinking and driving. You've just been drinking water, haven't you?'

'That's right, it's been so hot. Of course I'd be happy to drive.' Steph was quick to agree. What else could she say? She rather hoped that Robert's car wouldn't turn out to be a Ferrari or some other scary supercar, but after the hospitality shown to her by the family this was the least she could do.

Chapter 13

The others went off and Steph was left with Robert. He disappeared behind a screen to change into a clean dry shirt, and she wondered if he would expect her to go to the drinks party with him. She was wearing her freshly ironed dress that Waldorf had soaked on the first day and she felt she probably looked presentable, but she had a suspicion the other guests would all turn up dressed in their finest. But, irrespective of that, she had a feeling there would be journalists and photographers there and the last thing she wanted was to appear in the pages of the tabloids as the *playboy virtuoso's* latest lady friend. She decided that she would do well to avoid accompanying him. She was about to tell him this when she saw him emerge from behind the screen, struggling to retie his bow tie. She called him over.

'Can I help? I used to tie my dad's all the time.'

He came over and she reached up to catch the ends of the tie and fashion them into a bow. This of course brought her face to within a foot of his and she suddenly felt the butterflies return to her stomach in a crazy swarm. In an attempt to defuse the situation, she brought up the subject of the civic reception to come.

'You don't expect me to come along to this drinks thing, do you?'

'Of course I do.' He sounded as if he meant it.

She shook her head. 'It'll be terribly smart and I'm not exactly all glammed up, so I think the best thing will be for me to have a look around town and then find a bar near the town hall and wait for you there. If I give you my phone number, you can call me when it's all over. Hold still… there you go.' She finished tying the bow and stepped back, partly relieved, partly sorry not to be standing so close to him any longer. When he responded she was genuinely amazed at what he said.

'You really don't need to wait outside. Come in with me. You look gorgeous as you are.'

No sooner had he said it than she felt the colour rise to her cheeks. To her surprise, on glancing up, she couldn't miss the fact that he, too, was now blushing as he realised what he had said, and she suddenly felt an overwhelming urge to burst out laughing. The two of them were behaving like teenagers. So much for her being a grown woman and he an inveterate womaniser. She caught his eye for a moment and saw the corners of his mouth curl upwards into a slightly embarrassed smile. His bright blue eyes met and held hers, the twinkle in them rendering them, and him, all the more appealing as he qualified his statement.

'When I say you look gorgeous, you must understand that this should not be construed in any way as my attempting to objectify you or wishing to subject you to any form of sexual harassment. My observation was purely aesthetic and was not intended in any way to give offence. I went to a seminar on that kind of thing last year and I know how to behave.' He gave her a wink. 'Contrary to anything you may have heard.'

'It's all right. I don't feel in any way harassed.' Whatever his reputation, she couldn't help grinning back at him.

'And thank you for the compliment, but after a day walking around Florence and then an afternoon in the sun, I have few illusions about how I look. Anyway, if you don't mind, as I'm not dressed for it, I'd rather duck out of the reception. Is that okay with you?' She wondered if he would realise her real reason for not wanting to be seen with him.

'Of course. Totally up to you.' If he realised that it was because she didn't want to be mistaken for one of his infamous lady friends, he didn't show it. 'And thanks for the help with the tie.'

They had just finished exchanging phone numbers when a young woman came along to inform him that she had come to collect him for the short walk to the town hall for the reception. Robert picked up his jacket and pulled it on. 'Here's hoping they've got aircon in there.'

Steph left him outside the town hall and headed for the market where she spent a pleasant half hour browsing the different stalls. She ended up buying herself a pair of intricately formed silver earrings and took her purchase to a nearby bar where she sat down under a parasol and relaxed in the welcome shade. Her head was full of thoughts of this man who could so easily have been a candidate for her affections but was, she kept telling herself, potentially bad news. She ordered an ice coffee and did her best to switch to a different topic, but all her brain could come up with was the biopsy she would have on Tuesday – and that wasn't a happy thought.

In an attempt to distract herself, she picked up a well-thumbed copy of *La Nazione*, the local newspaper, and skimmed through the pages until her attention was caught by a headline underneath a photograph near the middle of the paper. It translated as *American Rock Star Photographed in Portofino* and the article beneath it related that Cody Havergill (61), had been spotted on holiday on the coast. The article went on to reveal that he had apparently just purchased a property in Italy and then proceeded to list a selection of outrageous things he had done during his rock 'n' roll years. Steph had to smile. From what she had seen of him on the boat, his days of causing mayhem were behind him.

Rob phoned just before eight and it was getting dark as they returned to his car. This turned out to be a rather nice BMW saloon, which was far smarter than any car she had driven before, but wasn't in the scary supercar league, thank goodness. He handed her the key and stood watching indulgently as she opened the door before offering her a word of advice.

'I think you'll find the steering wheel's on the other side.'

Glad the twilight was hiding her blushes, she opened the door wider for him and ushered him into the passenger seat with a mock salute. 'I offer a professional service. If you would like to take your seat, sir...'

'You're too kind.'

Steph went around to the left-hand side of the car and sank into the leather-clad driving seat. After a bit of fiddling with buttons to adjust the height and reach, she set about starting the car. The first discovery she made was that this wasn't done with the key but with a button on the dashboard. It was all rather nerve-racking, but Robert was sympathetic and helpful and she soon got the hang of it. One lesson she quickly learnt as they drove down the hill to pick up the motorway was that the accelerator pedal needed to be treated with delicacy to avoid squealing tyres and possible speeding fines. Certainly, compared to her mum's old Mini, this thing went like the clappers. After almost half an hour of threading her way through the evening traffic, she emerged onto the autostrada and was finally able to relax a bit. She glanced across at Robert.

'I hope I haven't frightened the living daylights out of you.'

'Very much the opposite. I feel like I'm in safe hands.'

This comment then set her mind wondering how it would feel to have him in her hands and she had to make a concerted effort to banish such conjecture and concentrate on the road. Gradually they started to chat; first about the concert and the reception, and then about all sorts of things from Waldorf the dog to her father. To her amazement, Robert had actually met him once while playing with the Royal Philharmonic.

'But he didn't tell me he had such a talented daughter.'

'Ha! Just because I can play the piano a bit!'

'Don't forget your expertise as a chauffeur.' She could hear the humour in his voice, and she had to struggle not to let herself fall for his charming manner just as so many women had already done. Apparently unaware of the effect he was having on her, he continued. 'As for the piano, from what my dad was telling me, you have a real gift – and not just for the modern stuff. He says you play classical equally well. *Complimenti*, as the Italians say. As for Royalty, he even described you as "the new Vince". And, believe me, he doesn't hand out compliments unless they're merited.'

Steph couldn't repress the little surge of pride and hope for the future that this produced in her. Could it really be that she might some day find herself sharing a stage with one of the greatest bands of all time? The idea was breath-taking, but she knew she would do well not to count her chickens.

It was almost nine thirty when they turned off the motorway onto the road over the hills towards Lerici. Steph was feeling a bit tired by this time but not too bad. She was happy that she and Rob – he had insisted she should call him that – had been able to talk naturally about so many things without any awkward silences. They hadn't discussed relationships – whether between him and his older brother, or his alleged legions of random girlfriends, or hers with Ethan – and she'd also avoided mentioning her trip to the hospital on Tuesday, but other than those grey areas, they had been able to talk more freely than ever.

Getting through Lerici at this time of night was relatively quick and they were soon on the winding coast road. As they approached the gates to the villa, he pointed towards them.

'Just park at the villa and I'll walk over to my place. I can pick up the car in the morning.'

She shot him a smile. 'No, as an experienced chauffeur I insist on taking you to your final destination. You'll just have to tell me where to turn off.'

The turnoff was barely a hundred metres further on. A gravel track led off to the right and they bumped along it to his house. When they reached the gates to his property these opened automatically, and she drove through and drew up outside his house. As the car stopped, a security light came on, illuminating the charming old brick building. She turned off the engine and stretched, staring through the windscreen at the house.

'What a beautiful place to live.' And it was. It wasn't a big house, but it looked as though it had always been there.

Sandwiched between a massive palm tree on one side and an olive grove on the other, it had bags of character, looked great and was very appealing – not dissimilar to its owner, but far less potentially dangerous. As she opened the car door, her ears picked up the sound of whining and barking from inside the house and she realised that Waldorf had recognised his master's car. She looked across at Rob as he came around to join her. 'Has Waldorf been stuck inside all day?'

'No, I dropped him off with Donatella before leaving. He loves being with her and she always spoils him rotten. I asked her to bring him back here before dark. That means he's been on his own for a couple of hours now, so I imagine he's going to be happy to see us.' He pulled out his keys. 'I don't know about you, but I'm hungry. If you don't mind slumming it, could I offer you something to eat?'

She had to think before answering. Clearly this invitation would involve going into his house and, unless you counted the Labrador, this would mean finding herself alone with a man whose dubious reputation with women preceded him. Reluctantly, she decided it was best to decline. 'Thanks, but I don't want to put you to any bother. I think I'd better get back.'

'It won't be any bother, and I'd be honoured if you'd join me.'

Steph's stomach had been rumbling for an hour now, and she knew she didn't want to trouble Cesare and Donatella at this time of night, so she took a deep breath and hoped she wasn't going to regret this. 'Well, thank you, I'd love to join you for a quick bite...' Hopefully he would get the message that this was all she was signing up to.

She followed him across to the hefty old front door and he unlocked it. No sooner had he opened it than the Labrador came charging out, tail wagging furiously, and stood up on his hind legs to greet his master enthusiastically. Spotting Steph, he then transferred his attentions to her and almost knocked her flat as he did so, but at least this time he was perfectly dry, and her dress didn't suffer as a result.

'Waldorf, leave the lady alone.'

Steph rather liked being called a lady. Ethan had called her a whole lot worse at times. 'Waldorf's fine. We're old friends now.'

The three of them went inside and Steph found herself in a big open-plan room with a kitchen area at one end and glazed arches along the wall facing the sea. The floor was made of old terracotta tiles and the vaulted ceiling was held up with an intricate pattern of interlocking wooden beams that looked like the upturned skeleton of an old ship. She went across to the windows and peered through the glass and saw the lights of Lerici and La Spezia curling away to the right while straight ahead and to the left everything was pitch black.

'How does ham, cheese and garlic bread sound? Or if you're hungrier, I could make an omelette, or I've got some of Donatella's tomato soup in the freezer.' She turned back to see Rob at the kitchen end of the room with his dog sitting at his feet, an expectant look on his face.

'Whatever you're having will be fine, thanks. Please don't go to any bother; I certainly don't need anything more than some garlic bread and cheese. You should have seen the size of the ice cream I had at lunchtime.' Her brain immediately homed in on the fact that they would both be eating garlic, so it wouldn't matter if they kissed, and she gave herself a telling off. Kissing this man was definitely not on the menu. Before leaping into some romantic fantasy with a most unsuitable man she would do well to stop and reflect on the impossibility of this leading to anything meaningful, even if he were to turn out to be interested in her. And, so far, all he had demonstrated was simple friendship. Mumbling 'Get a grip' to herself, she walked over to offer help.

'Can I get something, cut the bread, do anything?'

'There's a loaf over there, so you could cut a few slices and give Waldorf the crust if you like while I go and sort out my eyes. He knows he always gets the crust and he'll probably start drooling if he doesn't.' He headed for the door but stopped and looked back as she was reaching for the big round loaf of crusty white bread. 'And you could open a bottle of wine if you feel like it. There's rosé and white in the fridge, or red in the cupboard alongside. You decide. Corkscrew's in that drawer and the glasses are on the shelf above the sink.'

She sliced the bread and handed the crust to a grateful Labrador who disappeared with it to his basket in the corner of the room and started crunching it with evident satisfaction. Opening the fridge, she located a bottle of cold rosé, pulled out the cork and was filling two glasses when Rob returned, blinking. He had obviously ditched his remaining contact lens and was now wearing glasses. If anything, they added to his attraction, but she did her best to ignore such things.

'Better?'

'Thank God for that. I can see again.'

She set his glass down beside him and raised hers. 'Cheers, and thanks a lot for the offer of a meal.'

He picked up his glass and clinked it against hers, those sea blue eyes meeting hers for a moment or two as he did so. 'Hardly a meal; more of a snack really. Anyway, thank you for driving me back.' He was sounding very formal.

She took a sip of the wine and murmured appreciatively. 'Mmm, this is good. Is it local?'

'Sort of. I get my rosé and my white from a little man in Tuscany, and Cesare gets the red wine from a place he knows up in Piedmont.' He grinned at her. 'As I'm sure you know, Italians take their wine and food very seriously, and now that I'm a full-time resident over here I'm doing the same.'

'My dad was very happy living in London, but he never gave up his love for Italian food and wine. Although Mum's a very good cook, Dad used to love doing traditional Italian dishes and he taught me how to make stuff like risotto, potato gnocchi and all different types of pasta... oh yes, and how to make a real tiramisù. He had a whole lot of contacts in London who got him the right salami, the right cheeses and the right wine. He was from Venice so, of course as far as he was concerned, the best wine in the world was from that area. You know how territorial the Italians are about their food and wine.' Thoughts of her father dampened her mood and it must have shown on her face.

'Still miss him?' She nodded and he continued. 'Was he your inspiration for choosing to do music?'

'My mum plays the piano very well and she taught me a lot, but Dad was the one who pushed me to do all my grades even when, as a teenager, I was more interested in other things. I'm grateful to him now, even if I wasn't always at the time.' She took another sip of wine as Rob slid the slices of bread into the toaster and headed for the fridge. 'What about you? Your dad was your inspiration, presumably.'

He was digging in the fridge for cheese and ham and his voice was muffled. 'To an extent. Music's always been big in our family but growing up as the son of a rock star can have its downsides.'

'Such as?' She was delighted to hear him opening up to her.

'Such as being packed off to a snooty boarding school full of Hooray Henrys.' When he emerged from the fridge, he had located no fewer than five different cheeses and a package of sliced cured ham. 'You like *prosciutto e melone*?'

'That sounds perfect, thanks. You went to boarding school?'

'For four years until my folks finally settled down near Oxford. Before that they were zooming off all over the world. I hardly saw them, my father in particular, for months on end. For an eight-year-old kid it wasn't a bundle of fun.'

'I can imagine. Can I help with the melon?'

He reached into the fridge once more and emerged with a plump grey-green cantaloupe melon. 'If you don't mind, that would be great.'

She found a sharp knife and sliced the melon in half, revealing the succulent orange flesh inside. As she divided one half into slices and set about trimming them, she returned to the story of his life. 'How come you chose classical music? Surely all the influences must have been for modern stuff?'

'That was down to Mrs Dooley, my first great love.' He set about rubbing the slices of hot toast with a fat clove of garlic until this had disintegrated in his fingers. He then pulled out an old straw-covered Chianti flask and drizzled thick greenish olive oil from it onto the bread. Meanwhile, Steph was curious about his first great love.

'Tell me about Mrs Dooley. I hope her husband wasn't jealous.'

'Of an eight-year-old? I doubt it. She was the music teacher at school, and she rapidly became my mentor, surrogate mother and muse. We're still in touch, and I send her tickets any time I'm playing in the UK. She has trouble with her ears nowadays so she can't fly, or I'd get her over here. She would have loved this afternoon. Fiesole's a wonderful setting and Tchaikovsky always was one of her favourites. She was the first person to put a violin in my hands and I'll be eternally grateful to her.'

He looked up, a nostalgic expression on his face. 'The violin became my best friend at school. I used to hide myself away and play whatever came into my head and forget about the bullies, the loneliness, and the fact that I hardly ever saw my parents. I owe her a lot. When I left that awful school, she was the only thing I missed.' He sprinkled a pinch of salt over the slices of toast and looked up. 'Right, I think we're good to go. Shall we eat?'

They sat opposite each other at a table by the window. At her request, he dimmed the light above the table so that she could admire the view over the sea. This also had the advantage of limiting her view of him and those magnetic eyes – glasses or no glasses. There was no getting away from it: being with him felt really good. If it hadn't been for his reputation and the complications of their diverging career paths, she could easily have fallen for him. Big time.

While they ate, she realised that the sea in front of her was no longer completely dark as she had first thought. As her eyes became acclimatised, she made out the lights of a large cruise liner making its way up the coast a few miles out. She found herself wondering what Paganini would have made of a vessel carrying thousands of passengers. Back when this place was built, the only ships would have been powered by sails or oars alone.

By the time she and Rob reached the end of their meal, she felt she knew him a lot better and her affection for him had grown. She even found herself thinking that maybe a short-lived affair while she was over here might not be such a bad idea after all. No sooner had this thought crossed her mind than her Jiminy Cricket of a brain was already telling her she was crazy. The only thing this would bring would be heartbreak and, if the tabloids got hold of it, shame and ignominy. Besides, although she could feel *her* affection for *him* growing, so far he had been friendly, but nothing more. The fact was that he was a big name in the world of classical music and there were heaps of far more suitable and attractive women out there wishing for nothing more than to get together with him. Best to steer clear of him... but it wasn't easy.

At eleven o'clock he insisted on walking her back to her accommodation with Waldorf trotting happily in front of them and occasionally disappearing into the trees before reappearing once again, his eyes glowing green in the starlight. It was a warm night, but since the storm of a few days ago there was no longer that same suffocating heat. Autumn was slowly beginning to make its presence felt and she wondered what this place would be like in midwinter. One thing was for sure, however: she wouldn't be here to find out.

When they reached the door to the guest suite she stopped and turned towards him, unsure what was going to happen next. In spite of her conviction that getting involved with him would set her on a hiding to nothing, she also knew without a doubt, as she stood there on that warm Italian night, that if he were to kiss her she would respond. He turned towards her and there was an agonising hiatus of a few seconds that felt like hours, before he gave her a little wave and stepped back.

'Thanks, again, Steph.'

Repressing a stab of regret, she started breathing again and summoned a smile. 'Thank you for the meal and thanks for a wonderful afternoon. I'll always remember it.' She almost added, 'I'll always remember you,' but she didn't.

He didn't respond at once and it looked for a moment as though he was going to say or even do more, but in the end he must have thought better of it as he gave her a little smile before turning away.

'*Ciao*, Steph.' He and his dog were about to disappear into the darkness when she heard him add, almost under his breath, 'And I'll always remember tonight.'

Chapter 14

Next morning Steph got up a bit later than usual after what had turned out to be a good night's sleep once she had managed to get Rob out of her head and finally drop off. The good news was that thoughts of him had prevented her from obsessing about the upcoming biopsy. When she got up to the villa for breakfast on the terrace it was to find no sign of Ethan, whose bedroom door had been closed as she walked past. She had seen and heard nothing of him last night, and it was almost nine by now so she hoped he hadn't done anything stupid. She sat down opposite Keith and Faye and recounted how she had managed to drive Rob back safely and how he had given her dinner. Faye looked impressed but this was not, as it turned out, on account of her driving prowess.

'He actually invited you into his house?' Steph saw her exchange looks with Keith. 'But he behaved himself, right?'

Steph was quick to reassure them. 'He was a perfect gentleman.' She could see incredulity on Keith's face, but Faye looked remarkably satisfied.

'That's real progress. Maybe he's changing after all. Well done.'

Steph could feel the eyes of both of them on her, but she was saved by the arrival of Cesare from the house.

'*Ciao*, Stefania, you got back all right?'

She repeated what she had just told Rob's parents and saw a smile appear on his face. 'Very good. I'm glad you two are getting on. Now what can I bring you: your usual or something else? I've made a fresh fruit salad if you like.'

Steph thanked him and asked for a bowl of fruit salad and her usual cappuccino. As he went off, Faye made an observation. 'Of course, it's because you're also musical and from what Keith says, you like playing classical music.'

'That's what I was brought up on, but I love all kinds of music.'

'That's it, then. Being with you makes him feel comfortable.'

Steph was glad if she made Rob feel comfortable, but she knew that for her it could so easily have become more than that. In fact being with him was stimulating rather than comforting. Of course, she thought to herself, this explained why the kiss she had been half expecting last night hadn't materialised. Although *she* might be harbouring romantic notions – however inadvisable – *he* saw their relationship in a different, altogether more prosaic light. Quite simply: she was his comfort blanket. Nice as it was to know that she was offering support to another human being, deep down inside she almost regretted the fact that he hadn't tried to seduce her. No sooner had this thought registered with her than she realised how ridiculous it was. This man was trouble, and she would do well to steer clear of him. Besides, she was only here for another week or two and then that would be that. Nothing much should or would come out of it anyway.

'No Ethan this morning?' Keith's tone was so casual it screamed disapproval. 'I imagine he must be having a lie-in. Cesare tells me he and Willow went out clubbing last night, so God knows what time they got back. I didn't hear a thing.'

'Well, I did.' Faye gave a snort. 'It's all right for you. You've always been able to sleep through anything. The storm the other night hardly bothered you, did it? I heard them all right; Willow's heels clip-clopping up the stairs at half past three in the morning and then her screaming at Den about something or other. For God's sake, I ask you…' Her voice tailed off in exasperation.

To Steph's surprise, Keith burst out laughing. When his laughter subsided, he reached over and squeezed his wife's hand.

'Sorry, sweetheart, I'm not laughing at you being woken up in the middle of the night. I'm laughing at myself, at us. Look at us, would you? Ten, twenty years ago *we* would have been the ones up half the night, drinking, dancing, enjoying ourselves and clip-clopping about and shouting and screaming at ungodly hours.'

'And doing an awful lot of other stuff that we shouldn't have been doing.' Faye shook her head ruefully.

'And that. And here we are now: a couple of old fogies muttering darkly about the carryings-on of the young people. That's it, Faye, we're officially old.'

Now it was his wife's turn to laugh. 'Speak for yourself, grandpa. I'm four years younger than you and don't you forget it.'

As Steph listened to them she felt a wave of real affection for this kindly, welcoming couple. 'At the risk of speaking out of turn, I have to say that I think you guys are amazing. We all get old, if we're lucky, but how many older people are writing and performing new music, maybe even getting back on tour with a rock band, providing a guiding light for thousands, millions of people of all ages around the world. If that's being old fogies, I can't wait to be one.'

Faye gave her a gentle smile and Keith beamed. 'Dead right, Steph, and on that note, how's about you and I get together this morning to go through a few more of the new numbers before your boyfriend surfaces?'

In spite of her agreement with Ethan, Steph felt she owed them full disclosure. 'Great idea, Keith, but he's my *ex*-boyfriend.'

Faye caught her eye. 'I'm sorry to hear that, Steph. What brought that on, if you don't mind me asking?'

'It's been building up for some time. When I first met Ethan he was a great guy: caring, ambitious and hard-working. We got on really well together and I genuinely believed he might be The One. Above all, I thought he was someone I could trust. The trouble is that over the last year or so he's been getting into bad company and changing into a different, far more irresponsible person; somehow regressing into a more juvenile character. Sometimes I hardly recognise him… and I'm afraid I no longer trust him.'

Faye nodded sympathetically at her. 'Sort of the opposite of us. When I first met Keith, he was a wild one. I'm sure you must have read some of the stories about what he got up to, what the whole band got up to, but that was only the tip of the iceberg. It may seem hard to believe now but this soon-to-be old age pensioner was totally out of control.' She turned back and gave him a loving smile before her expression became more serious. 'You're lucky I came along when I did, darling, or it might not have been just Vince ending up dead.'

Keith leant over and kissed her tenderly on the cheek. 'Amen to that. But that was just the way it was back then.

Being in a band's a surreal lifestyle, Steph, especially when you're on the road, and we did a *lot* of touring. Some years I was away for more than half the time. One place just morphs into another, one hotel room into another, and I genuinely had to get one of the roadies to remind me where I was every night before I went on stage in case I got the name of the place wrong. It doesn't get the show off to a great start when you step out and shout, "Good evening Philadelphia!" and it turns out you're in Detroit. The trouble is that I'm afraid that's the lifestyle Ethan and, to some extent, our two boys have embraced. I hope they all find themselves a Faye – but I fear they broke the mould after they made you, sweetheart.' He kissed her again and then returned his attention to Steph. 'I'm sure you would have been what Ethan needed, but he just didn't realise it. He'll regret it with time.'

'I wonder.' Steph heaved a little sigh and then told them she had to fly home that evening for a medical appointment and so would be here today but not back until tomorrow night. As with Lottie, she ended up telling Faye what it was all about, and she received warm support from them both. It turned out that Faye had first-hand experience.

'Been there, done that. Biopsies are no big deal these days. I'm sure they're just erring on the side of caution.'

Her husband chimed in with more practical help. 'You're on the evening flight from Pisa? I'll get Cesare to give you a lift to the airport.'

Steph tried protesting, saying a lift to the nearby station would be fine, but Keith insisted that Cesare would drop her off and pick her up again when she returned the following evening, and she was genuinely touched by their kindness.

At nine thirty she met up with Keith in the studio and they played together for well over an hour before Ethan staggered in looking like death. Steph was genuinely worried for a moment or two until she realised that the ailment he was suffering from was self-inflicted. From the pallor in his cheeks, it looked as though all the blood had emptied out of them into his bloodshot eyes. He ran a weary hand through his unkempt hair and gave Keith an apologetic look.

'Sorry, man. I had a hard night.'

Keith nodded. 'I can see. A word to the wise: don't overdo it. Nobody's immortal. Anyway, Steph and I are just jamming so why don't you go and take a shower and get yourself a few cups of strong coffee? We're good here.' His tone wasn't unkind, but Steph could sense the annoyance below the surface. And who could blame him? He was paying their wages.

'Yeah, right, okay.' Ethan gave a feeble wave of the hand and staggered out again, leaving Steph wondering if she should apologise on his behalf. Keith saved her the trouble.

'I've been there. I feel sorry for the guy. I've seen that look before. If he carries on like that, he's going to need help.'

'When you say, "that look", do you think there's more to it than too much to drink?'

'I'm no medic, but I do have a lot of experience of some very scary stuff, and yes, I'm afraid it looks to me as though Ethan's doing drugs.'

'What, like regularly?'

'I've been watching him since he got here. For my money, he's developing a habit; maybe not every day yet, but regular.' He caught her eye. 'And before you say it, you wouldn't be the first person in history to have a partner on drugs without you realising it. If you still have any sway over him, see if you can get him to see somebody. I can give you names of some good people, a good clinic. Mention my name by all means. There's even a new wing with my name and Faye's on it.'

'Thanks, Keith, I'll try, although I doubt he'll listen to me. I'm sure it would carry a lot more weight if he heard it from you, so if you get the chance please don't hold back.' Keith had just gone further up in her estimation. It was good to see somebody trying to give something back. She already knew about his amazing concert for world hunger that had raised many millions, but she hadn't realised that he was also contributing to rehabilitating others. This only confirmed the impression she had been getting that he and his wife were remarkable people.

They played on and she was charmed by the softer, more poignant tone of some of the new stuff. It reflected the change in his outlook on life and she felt increasingly confident it would appeal immensely to traditional fans as well as introducing a slightly different, more grown-up Royalty to a whole new audience. The problem was that first they had to get Ben on board once more.

Ethan returned at twelve looking a bit more human and so she left the two men together while she went down to the beach for a paddle. Today there was no sign of the dog or his master and she struggled to fight the urge to walk up the path to his house. Much as she would enjoy seeing him again, she knew he was best avoided. Her phone interrupted her pensive mood. She pulled it out and saw that it was Sky calling.

'Hi there, Sky. Where are you calling from?'

'Hi, Steph, we're back in sunny Manchester. Well, actually, it's raining, but what's new about rain up here? How's things?'

It was good to hear from her. In the short time they had known each other, Steph had developed a real friendship with her. 'All good, thanks. You missed a great concert yesterday.'

'I'm sure. Rob really is a wonderful musician, isn't he?' There was a pause of several seconds. 'How're things going between the two of you?'

'Things are good, thanks.' Steph went on to relate the events of the previous day and Sky's reaction was the same as Faye's.

'He invited you in for dinner and he behaved himself? That's great, Steph, I'm so glad.'

'Your mum said she hopes this means he's moving on from his playboy lifestyle, but it could simply be that he doesn't fancy me or because I work for your father.'

'Like I said, I can see he likes you, so stick at it. If anybody can get the leopard to change its spots I know it's you.'

'That's easy for you to say. You've got *your* man.'

'On that subject, that's the other reason I was calling. What are you doing on the sixteenth of December? It's a Saturday.'

'Um, I have no idea. No plans as yet. Why?'

'That's my wedding day and I'd love it if you could come. Could you?' There was a momentary pause. 'Rob'll be there…'

'Even if he isn't, I'd love to come. That's really super of you and Tom, you hardly know me after all.'

'I know you better than you think. Now that you've definitely split from Ethan, can I take it you'll be coming on your own? I'm trying to sort out the seating plan and it would help me to know.'

'I'll be on my own and that's really sweet of you to invite me.'

'Great. It's going to be in a place just outside Moreton-in-Marsh, deep in the Cotswolds. I'll send you a proper invite.'

For lunch Steph just helped herself to a plate of salad and a slice of what Donatella called her spinach roll. This was an omelette made with eggs and grated parmesan, spread with cooked spinach and pieces of smoked ham, rolled up like a Swiss roll and carved into beautiful yellow, green and pink swirling rings. It tasted as good as it looked. She was gratified to see Ethan go and sit with Denver and Willow on a different table while she was joined at hers by Ben and his wife. Now that the anniversary festivities were over, Rob was nowhere to be seen and presumably he would be keeping his distance until his brother left. Over lunch she chatted with Ben and gradually brought the subject around to his music once more.

'I was wondering whether you've written any more new stuff. I'd love to hear it if you have. I still find myself humming that piece we recorded the other day.' For a second she caught Lottie's eye and read approval in it.

She was delighted to hear him answer straightaway. 'I've got three others, to be honest. The one I played you the other day's my favourite, but I'd like your opinion on the others. I'd be happy to play them to you and to hear what you think. When are you going to be around?'

'Well, Keith's been in the studio all morning, but he said he's got stuff to do this afternoon so I imagine it should be free if that suits you. I'll check with him. What time's good for you?'

'Aren't you going off to London?' Lottie remembered their conversation on Friday.

'Yes, Cesare's giving me a lift, but I don't have to leave until five.'

Ben glanced across at Lottie. 'In that case, let's go and do it right now. All right with you, hun?'

'Definitely all right with me, I'll come with you. Listen, Benny, I've got a surprise for you. I brought Clara-belle with me. You know I'm insanely jealous of your other great love, but I knew you couldn't live without her for long. Do you want to play Steph your new numbers on that?'

Steph saw him smile and a look of relief crossed his wife's face as he did so. 'Thanks, sweetie, there's only one woman in the world for me and that's you, but it would be great to give the old girl a little strum.'

Steph felt a surge of excitement. 'You would play your stuff to me on your famous guitar? That's amazing. This is probably the moment to make a big confession: when I was thirteen or fourteen I was playing a lot of piano, but I also flirted with guitar for a few months, and I always dreamt of getting myself a gold Fender exactly like yours. If I promise to be very, very careful, do you think I might be allowed to hold it for a few moments? That way, as soon as they figure out time travel, I can go back and tell spotty, pubescent Steph that things really do get better.'

A few minutes later Steph not only got the chance to hold the iconic electric guitar, but she even remembered a few chords and was able to play them. Although it was plugged in, it was on a minimal volume setting so the sound was far from its bellowing best, but it sent a shiver down her spine all the same. Keith and Johnny, fore-warned, stayed away while Ben played his new numbers.

Steph joined in from time to time while Ethan – now looking wide awake again – recorded all of it. It was almost four o'clock by the time Ben set his beloved Clarabelle reverently on the floor and stood up. He looked tired, but happy.

'Thanks, guys, I really enjoyed that. And, Steph, you're a natural, you know. You just get my music, and your accompaniment suits my stuff so well.'

Steph could feel her cheeks glowing. 'Thanks, Ben. I was just following your lead, but I enjoyed myself a lot as well.'

'Um, Ben...' They both looked across at Ethan who was sounding unusually hesitant. 'You know that song of yours we recorded the other day, well, I hope you don't mind, but I played it to Keith and Johnny. Was that all right?'

There was silence for almost twenty seconds – Steph counted them off on the clock on the wall – before Ben replied.

'I wondered if you would.' Another pause, this time a bit shorter. 'That's all right. I didn't ask you not to, after all.' Yet another pause. 'Well, go on, what did they say?'

'They loved it.'

Steph added her support. 'They really, really loved it. We all did.'

'That's cool.' Ben wasn't smiling but he didn't look unhappy, so Steph exchanged glances with Ethan who took the next step. 'They said they'd like to try playing along with it so we recorded their tracks and I mixed them all together. Would you like to hear the result?'

The silence was deafening for all of thirty seconds before Ben gave a cautious nod of the head and Ethan was quick to act. Steph felt sure he had had the track all keyed up ready to go in the hope of getting Ben's agreement.

As the slow bass intro filled the room, followed by Ben's voice as he sang the first lingering words, Steph did her best to watch his face without being too obvious. On the other side of the console, she could see Ethan doing the exact same thing. What they both saw was a fifty-year-old man with tears running down his cheeks mouthing the words as he listened to the other instruments join in and the voices of his two former band mates add their backing to his. By the end, you could have cut the emotional tension in the room with a knife and Steph could feel her own eyes filled with tears. As the last notes faded out, Ethan looked across at Ben and spoke in a low voice.

'Of course, this is just done on acoustic guitars with minimal percussion so it'll sound a lot different in a final version with full electric and some backing singers but, even so, we were all blown away by it. What do *you* think?'

To Steph's surprise Ben answered immediately. 'Absolutely great! Jesus, man, that sounds amazing.' A smile had formed on his face and his enthusiastic response almost raised a cheer. In an instant the tension in the room melted away and a surge of excitement ran through Steph. They really had something here and Ben liked it. Ben ran his hands across his face to dry the tears and wiped them on his shorts before catching hold of Lottie and hugging her as if his life depended upon it. She was in floods of tears herself and although Steph couldn't see his face, from the way Ben's shoulders were heaving, he must have been in a similar state.

They walked up to the terrace together and found Johnny and Keith sitting with Tara and Faye under the sunshades, chatting. When they got there, Ethan told them what had just happened, and Steph saw all four faces beam. Keith was the first to react.

'Ben, I'm so, so pleased. Johnny and I really loved it. Are you sure you didn't mind us adding our parts to see how it might sound?'

'Of course not. You did a great job and it sounded amazing.' Ben shot a glance across at Steph. 'All of you. You too, Steph. It was just like Vince never went away.' There was silence for almost a full minute before he carried on. 'I'm so glad you all like it. I wrote it from the heart.' His tone became a bit more subdued. 'I wrote it for Vince.'

'Does it have a title?' Keith sounded equally subdued.

'I've been calling it "For Vince", but just recently I had an idea. He's gone now and nothing can change that, but maybe the time's come for us to make a fresh start. I rather like the idea of calling it "Never Too Late". What do you think?'

'Sounds great, Ben, just great.' Keith came over and stretched his arm around his friend's shoulder. 'How about we sit down together tomorrow and do a bit of jamming? I've got some new stuff you might like to hear.'

'I'd like that.' Ben was smiling now.

Steph reminded them that she wouldn't be here, and they told her that wasn't a problem and wished her well. Lottie in particular jumped up and gave her a warm hug.

'Try not to worry, sweetheart, it'll all work out for you. You'll see.'

Steph gave her a grateful smile and went off to the guest apartment to get ready. Ethan walked with her as far as the studio and stopped at the door.

'Good luck for tomorrow, Steph.'

'Thanks a lot.'

'Sounds good about Ben, doesn't it?'

'It certainly does. So do you think this means Royalty are back up and running?'

'I hope so. Fingers crossed, but it's looking good. I think Ben's back.'

'And what about you, Ethan? Are you coming back?'

'Back from where?'

'You tell me.'

Chapter 15

The flight got into London at nine thirty that evening and by the time Steph got home it was gone eleven. It was lovely to see her mum again and they sat and chatted until long past midnight. She had broken the news of her break-up with Ethan to her mum a few days earlier and there was no need to say more. She knew how her mum felt about him. In the course of their conversation, Rob's name came up and she told her mum about the concert and the drive home to his house. Her mum subjected her to careful scrutiny.

'So much for him being a Casanova. It sounds like he behaved perfectly.'

'Or he just didn't fancy me.'

'Rubbish, he's just showing you he's not the man you think he is. Now you've had dinner at his house with him, what's the next step? Has he asked you out again?'

'No, and I doubt he's going to – and it's best that way.' Steph went on to repeat what Faye had said about her making Rob feel comfortable. 'And comfortable doesn't mean interested, at least not interested in an emotional way.'

Her mother shook her head. 'I know exactly what Faye meant. I always felt comfortable with your father, but that didn't mean I didn't love him. In fact, I loved him all the more because of it. I'd have hated to have one of those stressful marriages with sudden outpourings of emotion, constantly breaking up and making up. Passion's all well and good but comfortable is better; it really is.'

'I don't know... He lives in Italy, I'll be leaving soon, it could never work.' Steph hesitated before voicing her deepest fear. 'Besides which, what if this biopsy of mine throws up something sinister? Romance would be the last thing on my mind.'

'The biopsy will be fine. They do them all the time. And the doctor told you it could be just a cyst, didn't she?'

'But what if it isn't just a cyst?'

'Then they'll treat it. They can do amazing things these days. Try not to worry and don't start imagining the worst. As for Rob, if he really likes you...' She held up an admonitory hand to stop Steph from protesting. 'If he really likes you, he'll be there to support you through anything. Like I've always told you, you need to be positive and don't overthink things.'

'I know, Mum...'

Steph didn't sleep very well that night and she was up early; so early in fact that she had time to borrow her mum's car and drive over to Ethan's apartment. It took her well over an hour, but she managed to collect all her things from there and load them into the car. At least this way she wouldn't need to come back here again. Taking one last look around, she closed the door on that flat and on that chapter of her life.

The biopsy was remarkably quick and painless, and she was in and out of the hospital in less than an hour. The doctor who did the procedure reassured her that this was just to double-check and told her there was no cause to worry. Even so, Steph knew she would be on edge every day until the results came through, supposedly within a week or ten days. She had lunch with her mum in the local pub and then it was time to take the train back to the airport. As her mum kissed her goodbye, she repeated her mantra about being positive and not worrying about things she couldn't control. Steph nodded dutifully.

The flight was uneventful and on time and when she got back to Pisa there was a surprise in store for her. When the automatic doors parted and she walked out into the Arrivals area she saw a familiar, but unexpected, face waiting for her.

'Rob? What are you doing here?'

He gave her a welcoming smile. 'I'm on chauffeur duty today. Cesare told me you were flying back so I thought I could repay my debt by driving *you* home this time.'

She went over to him and came close to throwing her arms around him and giving him a kiss but restrained herself at the last moment and settled for a simple hand-shake.

'That's ever so kind of you. But aren't I taking you away from your rehearsing?'

'That's fine. I've been putting in a lot of practice, thanks. Besides, it'll be nice to have a bit of company for a change.'

While it was nice to be considered 'company' it wasn't exactly an outpouring of emotion but then, she reminded herself, she hadn't been expecting anything else. The car was parked in the short-term parking area close to the terminal and it was barely nine o'clock by the time they set off. All the way up the autostrada they chatted, and he revealed that his mother had told him why she had been in London.

'I'm sure it'll be fine. The doctors always want to make sure, to double-check.'

'Thanks, Rob, I hope you're right.' She reflected that this time he was the one acting as a comfort blanket and it felt good.

They reached Lerici just after ten, and he made a suggestion.

'I don't know about you, but I could eat something. If you're hungry, there's a great pizzeria just down here. What do you think?'

'I'd love a pizza. I had a Scotch egg and salad in the local pub at lunchtime, but I haven't eaten since. If you're sure you can spare the time, let's have a pizza.' The chances of being spotted with him and photographed by the paparazzi in a random pizzeria were very slight, after all. A thought occurred to her. 'What about Waldorf? He won't be chewing your place to bits by now will he?'

'If he's chewing anything, it'll be Mum's Persian rugs. I left him with them. He's fine.'

The pizzeria was close to the waterfront, and they were lucky enough to find a parking spot right outside. Inside it was lively and still crowded, but the proprietor, who clearly recognised Rob, found them a table in a corner and took their order. On Rob's recommendation she opted for a *Specialitá della Casa* pizza and wondered what it was going to have as a topping. When it arrived, barely ten minutes after they had sat down, it turned out to be a sort of Surf and Turf topping with the usual cheese and tomato but also smoked ham and sausage along with octopus and prawns. It tasted every bit as good as it looked. They both ordered cold beers and she thoroughly enjoyed the meal and the company. By the time she had finished her bowl of meringue and apricot ice cream and was sitting back with a little espresso, she knew Rob a lot better, even though they had stayed well clear of anything too personal.

Back at the villa they found Keith, Johnny and Ben still up, sitting in the lounge chatting. Stretched out at their feet was the Labrador. As he heard their footsteps, the dog jumped to his feet and came rushing over to greet first Rob and then Steph. As she patted Waldorf with one hand she gave the three men a little wave with the other.

'Hi, guys, how did it go today? Did you do a lot of playing?'

'Hi, Steph. We played pretty much all day. In fact, we've just come out of the studio now. Royalty is about to be reborn.' Ben was sounding animated, and Steph was delighted for him, for all of them. 'How about you? All go well?'

'Yes, thanks. No problems.' There was no point telling them she still had ten days to wait for the results. 'That's fantastic news about Royalty getting back together again. You're going to make millions of people really happy, starting with me. So, what's the plan for tomorrow? More of the same?'

This time Keith answered for the band. 'If you're up for it, we thought we might have a go at getting a near final version of one or two of them recorded up. We're going to have to contact the record company pretty soon to give them the news and it would be good to have a few numbers in the can before we do. Are you going to be okay to take part tomorrow?'

'I most certainly am. I can't wait.'

Beside her, Rob glanced at his watch. 'I'd better make a move. See you tomorrow.'

He was already turning for the door, accompanied by the dog, when Steph managed to get in a few words of thanks for collecting her from the airport. He gave her a little smile and a wave and disappeared.

When Steph went down to the beach next morning, it was with a renewed sense of optimism for the future, at least as far as her professional life was concerned. As far as her health was concerned, she was doing her best to heed her mother's advice and try not to think about it, but it wasn't easy. As for the violinist up on the headland she was convinced now more than ever that he wasn't interested in her as anything other than a friend – an increasingly good friend but just a friend.

At the hospital they had told her not to swim for a few days, so although her bikini neatly masked the surgical dressing, she just waded into the sea until the water was up to her knees. Although they were well into September, the water temperature was still delightful, and it soon emerged that she wasn't the only one to think so. A black shape came charging down the narrow path from the cliff top at breakneck speed and gave a volley of loud woofs before plunging into the water. Steph smiled as the Labrador doggy-paddled towards her and prodded her with his nose.

'*Ciao, bello*. It's good to see you.'

A shout from above made her look up again.

'Steph, hey, do you want a coffee?' It was the dog's master who was looking to see what Waldorf had been barking at. He was standing at the top of the path, and she saw him point towards the beach. 'I'll come down.'

Steph felt a little pulse of pleasure to see and hear him and she waded back to the shore accompanied by her canine companion. By the time she reached the beach, Rob was already standing on the sand and this time she was the one to emerge, dripping, from the water. The feel of his eyes on her as she stepped out of the shallows aroused a series of emotions in her, ranging from embarrassment, to excitement, to good old-fashioned lust. She had never been one of those girls who enjoyed showing off her body and she felt decidedly awkward, knowing that only two minimal pieces of material separated her from being completely naked. Nevertheless, she did her best to appear nonchalant as she raised a hand and gave him a little wave.

'Hi, Rob.'

'Hi, Steph, looking good.'

She felt her cheeks flush. 'I've just fallen out of bed, but thanks anyway, and I'd love a coffee.' She could have told him he looked good as well, but she controlled the urge.

He glanced at her wet legs. 'You're soaking wet and the path up to the house is very rough even in flipflops. Unless you've got leather-soled feet or shoes, you're going to find it hard work getting up there. I could always carry you, of course, but maybe it's better if you wait here for a few minutes and I'll bring the coffees down to the beach.'

The idea of being picked up and carried by him, clinging to his body, was enough to make her cheeks colour all the more. 'If you really don't mind bringing the coffee down here, that would be very kind, thanks. I'll dry myself off and talk to Waldorf while you're gone.'

He was true to his word and returned less than five minutes later with two little espresso coffees. By this time the dog was sprawled on the sand at Steph's feet, grunting happily to himself as she scratched his tummy with her toes.

'Waldorf's really taken to you, hasn't he?' Rob handed her a cup and stood alongside her, looking down at the dog. Behind him the tiny waves sighed as they touched the shore.

'I love him to bits, but you're going to have a terrible job getting all the sand out of his fur now that he's been rolling about on the beach.'

'No problem. All I have to do is throw a stick into the water and by the time he's swum out and brought it back a few times, he'll be all clean again – although I do hose him down to get the salt out every now and then.' He transferred his attention out to sea. 'What a gorgeous day. It's hard to believe we're already in meteorological autumn.'

Steph stifled a giggle. Now he was the one talking about the weather. 'The water's a perfect temperature.' Certainly, nobody could accuse this conversation of being too intimate.

As they sipped their coffees Rob repeated how pleased he was that it looked as though Royalty were about to be back up and running once more. 'Dad must be over the moon. I take it this means they're going to press on with the new album?'

'That's what we're hoping. I think the plan is to carry on jamming all day today and maybe record a couple in their near final form, so I'm keeping my fingers crossed.'

'And Dad's confirmed that you've agreed to play keyboards for them. I bet you never thought you'd end up doing that.'

'For a legendary band like Royalty? Not even in my wildest dreams.' She smiled at him. 'I was telling my mum the other day that all those hours spent listening to Royalty in my room weren't wasted after all. Don't get me wrong: I had friends, but my room's where the keyboard was. We didn't have space in the house or we would have loved having a grand piano – assuming Mum and Dad could have afforded it, which is unlikely. If I'm ever somewhere with a grand I jump at the chance to play it. You can't beat the sound.'

'So would you say classical music is your first love or are you a modern music woman?'

Steph thought about it for a moment. 'I suppose I would have to say that if it's music to be listened to casually, I mostly prefer modern. But if it's for playing, I love playing classical, particularly Chopin, almost anything by Chopin.'

He looked straight at her for a moment, and she struggled hard not to let the bright blue eyes overwhelm her. There was no getting away from it: she could so easily get hooked. Apparently unaware of her inner turmoil, he came up with a tantalising suggestion.

'Two things: first, I've got a rather nice grand piano up at my place – although the sea air plays havoc with the tuning – which you're welcome to come and play any time and, second, I'm performing in Sanremo and a few other places next week and I'm including a selection of Chopin's nocturnes. I know he mostly wrote for the piano but I like to shake the audience up a bit, so I've adapted several pieces for piano *and* violin. I don't suppose you might have a bit of free time to accompany me for an hour or two as I practise? It would be a great help.'

Steph shook her head apprehensively. 'No way. I'm miles out of your league. Don't forget, I've heard you play.'

'I'm sure you could do it. I'm not asking you to launch into Beethoven's Sonata in B flat major or anything like that. All I want is a bit of accompaniment. I've only performed this once before and I'm a bit rusty. My regular accompanist will be meeting me in Sanremo on Saturday for a final practice so this would be just to give me a bit extra. Besides, the piano part is pretty straightforward. You do read music, don't you?'

Steph nodded. 'Yes, but…'

'Honestly, it'll be fine. Would you at least be prepared to come round and give it a try? It would be a big help. And if you don't feel comfortable doing it, you could always have a go on the Steinway anyway.'

Still feeling apprehensive, she reluctantly agreed. Her reluctance, she knew full well, was partly at the thought of accompanying a world-famous soloist, but it was also at the thought of finding herself once more alone in his charming old house with him. There was a limit to the amount of self-control she could muster if it were to turn out that he thought of her as more than a friend after all. He could see she was still having second thoughts, so he added an incentive.

'How about this as a deal? You give me two hours of your time today or tomorrow and I'll take you out to dinner in a lovely little restaurant I know in the hills in return?'

By this time the sensible, logical side of her brain had checked out completely so, in spite of all her doubts and fears, she said yes. After adding another handful of caveats about her limited skills, she agreed to come to his house as soon after five as she could that evening, subject to Keith and the others not needing her.

When she got up to the villa, she was delighted to find not only Ethan but also Ben, Johnny and Keith already at the breakfast table although it was barely half past eight. As she sipped her cappuccino, she asked Keith if they were still planning on playing all day.

'Yesterday went really well, so let's do more of the same but with you in the mix as well. We went through most of the new stuff yesterday, making a few alterations and additions and the next step is for you to join in with us. Maybe Ethan could even record one or two numbers although it'll still be just practice for most of them for the next few days until we've cracked them one by one. Okay with you?'

Steph shot a look across at Ethan who gave her a silent nod of the head. He looked better today, and it was obvious that he had managed to get up in time to take a shower and change into clean clothes before breakfast, which was progress. She looked back at Keith.

'Absolutely fine by me. I'll be down at the studio waiting.'

The day passed in a flash. They spent all morning in the studio and went through the ten new tracks, several of which rapidly developed into almost ten minutes each. Ethan demonstrated his skill as a producer by suggesting, cajoling, and bullying them, chopping out parts and editing others until the songs were all taking shape. Keith, contrary to how he had been reputed to behave, appeared happy to go along with almost everything and didn't raise his voice once. Although by the time they finished they had only been able to produce a final version of two of them, the different songs were all coming along well and the three band members went off with smiles on their faces. For Steph it had been a magical day, listening to these men – who had been her teen idols – discussing their work, and seeing first-hand how the different songs developed organically.

Lunch was a hurried affair and the only surprise was the absence of Willow. Faye whispered to Steph that

Willow had gone off somewhere the previous day and had only returned at nightfall and had barely exchanged two sentences with anybody. Whether this was because of a prior commitment or whether the shouting match in the middle of the night with Denver on Sunday had caused her to distance herself from him was unknown, but the fact that she had gone off again without him today sounded ominous for her hopes of marrying him. As for Denver, he appeared distracted as he listened to his father discussing the morning's session with the others. It looked very likely that something had happened to love's young dream.

Chapter 16

At the end of the afternoon, Steph went up to the villa to tell Cesare that she would be eating out, and then returned to her room, took a careful shower making sure not to get the dressing over her stitches wet, and changed in preparation for the evening. The idea of accompanying Rob on the piano worried her and she hoped he wouldn't be too disappointed if she failed to do it properly. Add to that her nervousness at the prospect of what might even be a proper date with him afterwards and she was unusually tense when she finally left her room and headed for his house. It was still hot outside so she had resisted the urge to dress up for him and decided in favour of one of her new tops and a pair of white jeans, although at the last minute she picked up a light jumper just in case it got colder inland as night fell.

She was greeted boisterously by the Labrador, who had been snoozing in the shade of one of the cypresses that lined the drive to the house. Walking between the trees, the aroma of resin was heady, and she breathed deeply as she looked through the dark green branches towards the blue of the Gulf of Poets beyond. It really was a fabulous location for a house. At her side, the happy dog bounced up and down, giving her a warm canine welcome.

'*Ciao*, Steph, thanks for coming.' Rob appeared at the door wearing a plain white T-shirt, shorts and a smile.

Certainly, she thought to herself, he appeared to be much more relaxed in her presence now that they were getting to know each other better. He appeared to be on his best behaviour, but she cautioned herself to be careful not to get drawn under his spell, but her subconscious was once again showing signs of rebellion.

'*Ciao*, Rob.'

She managed to restrain the urge to kiss him – even just on the cheeks – and followed him inside, through the big living room where they had eaten the other night and into another large room beyond. The far end of this was occupied by a magnificent concert grand piano, almost three metres long, its lid propped up so the strings were facing a pair of arched French windows that were wide open towards the gulf. The sight of this wonderful instrument only added to the butterflies in her tummy, and she glanced across apprehensively at him.

'What a monster, Rob! Where did you get this; the Royal Albert Hall?'

'Not far off. It actually used to belong to La Scala in Milan. I was performing at the opera house a couple of years ago and I heard that they were thinking of replacing their old piano after almost eighty years, so I took the plunge and said I'd buy it off them.' He grinned. 'As investments go, it has two advantages: one is that with that sort of provenance it's an appreciating asset, or so I'm told, and the other is that any would-be thief would need a forklift to get it out of here.'

Steph went across and ran her fingers reverently over the mahogany case. 'So do you play the piano as well as the violin?'

'Yes, but not particularly well. I do enjoy it, though. By the way, I find it's best played with the windows open otherwise it tends to echo a bit too much in here. Go on, see what you think.'

Nervously, Steph sat down on the antique music stool and let her fingers run lightly over the keyboard. The thought that some of the most legendary names in classical music had played on these same keys was awe-inspiring and she came close to jumping up and running off in alarm, but knowing how proud her father would have been to see her here, about to accompany one of the world's greatest living violinists, kept her glued to the seat. After a few seconds to collect herself, she launched into one of her favourite go-to pieces, coincidentally one of Chopin's nocturnes. It started slowly and gradually built up. At first, she was hesitant but then as her confidence grew and the rich sound of the historic piano filled the room, she let it take her and by the time she came to the last few notes she felt sure she had hardly ever played it so well.

She slowly lifted her hands from the keyboard and turned to give him an apprehensive look. In response he gave her what looked like a genuine smile. 'Lovely, really lovely. That's his Nocturne in D flat major; I've always loved that piece. It's not on my list for next week, but I play it myself on the piano from time to time, but never as well as that.' He gave a very Italian kiss of his pinched fingers. '*Bravissima!*'

A wave of relief swept over her. She knew he had to be exaggerating but it was wonderful all the same to receive a compliment from an artist of his calibre. 'So, what about this job you want me to do?'

'You're sitting on it.' He was grinning.

At first she didn't realise, and then the penny dropped. Rising to her feet, she lifted the cushioned seat to reveal the compartment beneath where she found a pile of sheet music, the top ones all Chopin.

They started with the Nocturne in C sharp minor and worked through three other pieces. She soon settled into the accompanist role and rapidly found that they worked well together. She was worried at first that he might develop into a pernickety tyrant, like his father had once been, according to Ben. She remembered her father telling her about some of the artists and conductors with whom he had worked who had shouted and screamed, but such was far from the case. Rob was understanding and very good at explaining exactly what he wanted her to do. She was fascinated to hear the way he tailored his playing to the original piano score, and she had to concentrate hard to keep her mind on what she was doing rather than what he was doing.

To her amazement, all too soon there came a time when she started having trouble reading the music, and it was only when he reached the end of the piece they were playing that she realised the sun had almost set and shadows were invading the room. He also saw that it was time to stop.

'Wonderful, thanks. You can't imagine how helpful that's been. Sorry to have taken so much of your time; it just flew by. Feel like some dinner?'

Steph glanced at her watch and saw that they had been playing nonstop for well over two hours. She stood up and stretched. 'Sounds good to me.'

Rob led her into the living room where the dog was stretched out on the terracotta tiles sleeping soundly, and pointed across to the fridge. 'Help yourself to a cold drink. There's beer, wine, whatever you want in there. I'm just popping upstairs to put on a fresh shirt. I don't know about you, but I'm sweating buckets.'

Steph waved him away and went over to the fridge. As she did so, she immediately found she had a black shadow at her side, suddenly wide awake and quite clearly hungry. She wasn't sweating but she helped herself to a glass of cold mineral water and sipped it while trying to explain to the dog that she didn't know where his food was or she would have given him something. Rob's voice from the door interrupted her conversation with Waldorf.

'That's a thought. I'll feed him before we go out. That way he can come with us and sleep under the table without pestering us.'

He had changed into a fresh blue polo shirt. The colour suited him, and he looked as appealing as ever. She took the final gulp of water as the thought registered with her that this was the moment their date started – if that was what it was.

The Labrador vacuumed up his food in seconds and after a brief walk in the garden, marking his territory, he was bundled into the car and they set off. Steph settled back in the passenger seat as they bumped along the track towards the coast road and then turned left towards Lerici.

'Where are you taking me?' Not that she minded in the slightest where they went. A Michelin-starred restaurant or a McDonalds would be fine with her, or anywhere as long as it wasn't a flashy place where they might be spotted and photographed together.

'Uphill.' He went on to explain. 'The plan is to head inland, and around here that means uphill into the Apuan Alps. Don't worry, it's not too far. About half an hour max.'

He wasn't joking about the hills. From the moment they passed under the main north–south autostrada and got onto a minor road, they started to climb and didn't stop climbing for almost a quarter of an hour. As the road snaked ever higher via a series of hairpin bends, the sun disappeared beneath the horizon behind them, but not before she had had time to look back down at the spectacular view of the gulf below as they drove through a succession of olive groves. When they neared their destination Rob told her about the restaurant.

'It's a tiny little place Cesare and Donatella told me about years ago. It's owned by a guy called Beppe and his wife, Ines. They have a little smallholding, make sensational olive oil and, if you ask very nicely, they're sometimes prepared to cook dinner. I phoned him earlier and fixed it up. I hope you like it.'

The restaurant itself was unlike any Steph had ever been to before. To get to it, Rob turned off the road and bumped along an even more potholed track than the one leading to his house until they reached what looked like little more than a wooden hut amid the olive trees. As they drew up, a scruffy terrier came scurrying out of the shed, barking ferociously. Steph glanced apprehensively at Waldorf who was on his feet behind her in the car, staring out, but saw that his tail was wagging. Presumably these two knew each other. In fact, when Rob let him out, the two dogs had a wonderful time chasing each other about while the elderly proprietor emerged and shook hands warmly with Rob and then Steph, before showing them to their table underneath a vine-covered lean-to. There were only two other tables and both were empty. They had the place to themselves.

From here in daytime they would have had a clear view all the way down the hillside to the coast. Now that it was dark, all they could see were lights of a handful of villas and farms dotting the hillside and the brighter lights of the towns at sea level. Around them were only olive trees and, apart from the sound of the dogs as they charged about, all was silent. It was a delightful spot.

'What do you think?' Rob's voice returned her attention to him, and she gave him a broad smile.

'It's amazing. What a place.'

'Wait till you try the food. We're not talking fancy food with all sorts of bells and whistles. It's good solid country fare: no frills, but it's all genuine. You know the Italians love to describe their food as *genuino*, and that's what this place is: authentic and natural. The food we're going to get should be fresh, local and prepared in the traditional way.'

'I can't wait.' After her salad lunch, a busy day, and the stress of two hours of accompanying him on the piano, she was hungry.

As it turned out, that was just as well. Within two minutes of their sitting down Beppe returned with a huge plate of hand-carved ham and salami. Along with it were slices of melon, fresh black figs and a pot of soft goat's cheese. Seconds later he came back again with an unmarked bottle of red wine, a bottle of water, a basket of focaccia bread and a candle stuck in an old Chianti flask that he positioned on the table between them. He mumbled a quiet *buon appetito* and withdrew.

Steph asked Rob about the upcoming concerts and was disappointed to hear that he would in fact be leaving in just two days' time. This was to be for a little tour of the Ligurian coast, starting in Sanremo and followed by other performances including Genoa and Savona the following week, which meant he would be away for a total of six days, not coming back until next Thursday.

'This time of year's quite a busy time for me with outdoor concerts all over Europe and then later on there's a big Vivaldi festival in Venice, Puccini in Rome, Wagner in Berlin, and so it goes on.'

It hadn't escaped Steph's mind that by the time he came back the following week she would probably only have a matter of days before her flight back to the UK. 'What about Britain? Any performances planned?'

'November, I'm in London for a few nights.' He looked up from his melon. 'If you give me your address, I'll send you tickets if you're interested.'

Steph nodded mutely. Kind as the offer of tickets was, this hardly qualified as any indication that he might want to see her again once she left. Reminding herself that this was probably for the best didn't help. She took a sip of wine and tried to swallow her disappointment along with it.

The antipasti were followed by *pappardelle ai carciofi*. The wide strips of pasta arrived covered in a creamy sauce made with fresh artichokes from Beppe's garden and it was delicious. By the time she had finished the generous portion Beppe served her, Steph was beginning to feel full, and she enquired cautiously if there was going to be anything else to eat. In response, Beppe's wife, Ines, put in her first appearance of the night as she brought them a local speciality: *baccalà alla pisana*. This was a succulent mix of salt cod – for centuries the staple of mariners around here – cooked with potatoes, tomato, onions, olives and capers and, despite feeling full, Steph had to have some and was pleased she did. It was exquisite.

She just couldn't find space even for a small serving of *castagnaccio* as dessert, much as she liked this chestnut-based creamy sweet, and asked for an espresso instead. When Beppe brought them their coffees he also brought an anonymous bottle of clear spirit with the explanation that this was his own homemade grappa. She and Rob just took tiny taster sips of this firewater and had to admit that it was excellent, but definitely not the sort of thing to be drunk before setting off down a road full of hairpin bends.

Throughout the meal she and Rob chatted, and he told her about the tragic death by drowning of the poet Percy Bysshe Shelley somewhere just off the coast from his house. Apparently the poet and a friend had gone sailing in an unseaworthy boat in bad weather and the result had been his death at the age of only twenty-nine, coincidentally the same age as she and Rob were now. It was a sobering thought. Paganini, on the other hand, had survived until the age of forty-seven but spookily at the age of twenty-nine had contracted syphilis. Steph hoped this wasn't a bad omen and did her best not to let her mind dwell on her biopsy and the possible ramifications of a bad result.

Maybe realising that the conversation was becoming a bit morbid, Rob changed it to the more immediate matter of her future.

'What will you do if Dad and the others decide to go off on a world tour and they want you to go along in Vince's place? That would mean a big upheaval for you, wouldn't it?'

'I'm trying not to even think about it. The idea of me appearing on stage with a world-famous band like Royalty is too crazy for words. Can you imagine little old me up there alongside them? That sort of thing doesn't happen to ordinary people like me.'

'We're all ordinary people at heart, but you've got a real gift when it comes to playing the piano. Dad told me so and I could hear it for myself this evening. No, if he asks you to tag along, it'll be because you're worth it and you'd do really well. So… what would you say if he asked you?'

Steph had already spent many long hours debating this exact same question. The prospect was enticing and exciting and also fraught with problems, but there was only one logical answer. 'I'd have to say yes, but I'd go into it with my eyes open. I've seen enough burnt out, drink- and drug-wrecked musicians to know what a life on the road can do to people. Look at your own father and the others. Think of Vince. Sex, drugs and rock 'n' roll; traditionally they go together.'

'You're worried you could end up burnt out physically, mentally and maybe even morally?'

'It's a real risk.'

He caught her eye and held it in the candlelight. 'You're afraid you'd lose your moral compass?' Seeing her give a hesitant nod, he shook his head firmly. 'That's never going to happen to you. You aren't some clueless kid, fresh out of school with stars in your eyes. You're a grown woman and you'd be able to handle it, I'm sure of that. Besides, Dad and the others are no longer part of that scene. Look at them, Steph: they're old men. Well, all right, not *old*, old, but certainly a lot wiser than they used to be. I'm sure it would go well for all of you.' He took a mouthful of wine. 'And when it comes to loss of moral compass, you're talking to an expert.'

'In what way?' Although she already knew the answer.

'You know my reputation, right?' He didn't wait for her to confirm or deny it. 'I've spent the last few years living a hedonistic lifestyle.' He hesitated. 'I found myself living an artificial, superficial life. That's okay for a while, but then the day comes when you realise there has to be more.'

She smiled at him. 'Your sister was saying the exact same thing only the other day.'

He looked up and she saw him smiling back at her in the candlelight. 'She spent most of the summer having a go at me, but it's only lately that the penny's dropped and I know she's right. There has to be more.'

She nodded slowly; her eyes trained on the candle flame that was barely stirring in the evening air. 'That's the other problem I would face if your dad and the others really did offer me a place playing with the band. It's the whole question of settling down. How could I even think of making a life for myself with a home and a husband and kids if I'm off all over the world all the time?'

'That's what you'd like: to get married and have kids?'

She paused. This was something she had never voiced out loud to anyone before, not even to her mum and certainly not to Ethan. 'Like I said before, I'm ordinary. Ordinary people like me want to settle down and have a family.' She looked up from the candle flame. 'Like I told you, I'd be crazy to turn down an offer to join Royalty, but deep down I suppose I'm scared it might be disastrous for me, long term.'

'At the risk of repeating myself, I know you could handle it. If they ask you, say yes. You've got to embrace life. We're only on this planet for a short time and – carpe diem – we need to seize the day. Who knows what awaits us?'

She shivered. In spite of her mother's advice, a frightening premonition of herself in a hospital bed, linked up to monitors and drips as she slowly faded away, sent an apprehensive shudder throughout her whole body. He must have realised the way her mind was working as his hand reached over and caught hold of hers, giving it an encouraging squeeze.

'Sorry, I'm sounding far too solemn. I don't know why I'm talking about this sort of stuff. You've got your whole life ahead of you and it's going to be a wonderful life. I promise.'

'You do?' Her voice was almost choked with emotion.

'I do.' He looked deep into her eyes and gave her hand an encouraging squeeze. 'It'll be great.'

A movement from underneath the table was followed by a heavy paw landing on her thigh. She looked down to see the Labrador sitting at her side, staring up at her, the candlelight sparkling in his eyes, as he offered a bit of canine support. She caught hold of the big black paw with her free hand and gave it a little squeeze.

'You know something, Waldorf? You're a very good dog.' She looked back across the table at his master. 'He's amazing. He must have sensed my mood.'

'He really does. Sometimes, when I'm feeling a bit blue, he'll suddenly turn up at my side and give me a nudge with his nose or put a paw on my lap. I know some people say dogs are just dumb animals, but having another living creature who appears to understand and share your pain means an awful lot. Getting him was the best thing I could possibly have done.' He took a big swig from his water glass. 'We all need a bit of support from time to time.'

'Well, thank you for yours.'

He must have realised that he was still holding her hand and released it, but she immediately caught hold of his again. 'If you ever need me to return the favour, just shout.'

'One of these days I might just take you up on that.'

She gave his hand one more squeeze before releasing it and they sat in silence for several minutes before he caught her eye again. 'Time to go?'

She nodded so he called Beppe over, thanked him warmly and paid. Before going back to the car, they took a few steps into the olive grove and stood staring down at the lights on the coast far below. It was almost completely silent up here, apart from a chorus of chirping cicadas in the background, and she gradually became aware of tiny little yellow flashes flitting among the trees as fireflies went about their business. It was a wonderfully romantic location and under different circumstances she wouldn't have hesitated to catch hold of him and hug him to her. Her awareness that this relationship could never go anywhere was enough to hold her back so she deliberately, if reluctantly, turned away from him to pet the dog.

As they drove back along the track to the main road, she thanked Rob for the meal, and he waved away her thanks. They chatted in desultory fashion about trivia on the way down the hill, but the return journey was accomplished in almost complete silence, and she spent most of it reflecting on what he had told her. Was his sister right? Did this mean he was a changed man and, if he was, what might that mean for her? Although, apart from a brief touch of the hand, there was still no evidence that he thought of her as anything more than a friend and an accompanist.

When they got back to the coast, he didn't head for his house but drove through the gates to the villa and dropped her off at the top of the steps leading down to the guest apartment. He didn't turn off the engine, so she took the hint and reached for the door handle.

'Thanks, again, for a super meal. I really enjoyed this evening, Rob. Thank you.'

'You're welcome. And thanks for your accompaniment on the piano. That helped a lot.'

'If you need me to do it again, just say the word. You know where to find me.'

'Thanks.' She couldn't miss the fact that he didn't ask for more help.

Neither of them made a move even to shake hands, let alone kiss, so she opened the door and climbed out, reaching back in to ruffle the dog's ears as she did so.

'Goodnight, Waldorf, goodnight, Rob.'

To her surprise, his hand reached out and caught hold of hers. 'Good night, Steph, it's been a wonderful evening.' He raised her hand to his lips and kissed it softly before releasing her and returning his hands to the wheel. As he drove off, she could still feel the imprint of his lips on her skin and it felt good. Very good.

Chapter 17

That night she found it difficult to get off to sleep. Apart from the anticlimactic way the evening had ended, she found herself thinking about the scenario Rob had voiced. What if Keith and the others really did ask her not only to play with them for the album but to join the band and go touring with them? First and foremost, this would no doubt result in her making a lot of money. She would probably get a heap of money for every performance and maybe even a cut of the sales revenue of the album. Alternatively, they might just offer her a hefty annual salary, but this would most probably be much more than she was earning at present – and that would be hard to turn down.

There was of course the question of how long this might last. Keith was almost sixty and the others members were in their fifties so theoretically the band could very well keep going for another ten, even twenty years. After all, the Rolling Stones were still touring, and Mick Jagger was almost eighty. In twenty years' time she would be fifty and her chances of settling down and having a family would have all but disappeared. Could she realistically hope to balance being a member of a world-famous band with a life of domestic bliss? Even if that were possible, there was the minor problem of finding the right man first. And the one she thought she might have found here didn't appear to feel the same way about her.

The other big unknown was what the biopsy might reveal. If Keith and the others did offer her a place in the band, she might find herself saying yes to her great opportunity only to have to say no only a week or two later if the doctors told her she had cancer.

She got up feeling a bit jaded and went out for a walk, deliberately keeping away from Rob's house. She didn't want to put him in an awkward position. Last night had been going so well until he had started talking about death and she had had that premonition which had darkened her mood, but when she thought about it analytically, he hadn't made a move of any kind before that, so he either just didn't fancy her or he accepted the reality of the situation that within a matter of weeks or even days she would leave and that would be that.

She wandered about, enjoying the relative cool of the early morning air but noticed that grey clouds were approaching from the west. In fact, by the time she came back to her room, the sky had darkened as the cloud cover thickened. Still, she told herself, it was September after all.

Up at the villa at breakfast time the three band members were once again up bright and early and raring to go. Fortunately, so was Ethan and for the second day running he was looking and sounding on the ball. They were down in the studio just after nine and they worked all morning, not even stopping for a mid-morning coffee break. Ben was a changed man; joining in with the discussions, making suggestions and demonstrating that his musical talents hadn't diminished over the past ten years. Steph was pleased to find that the men included her in their deliberations and appeared to appreciate her input. As for Ethan, he worked the controls masterfully as they set about recording a couple more songs in their near final form.

That evening the rain started and dinner was served indoors. Before the meal they reconvened in the lounge and Keith played back the recordings for everyone to have a listen, and looking around, Steph got the feeling that everybody liked the new music a lot. This even included Willow, who had reappeared from wherever she had been the previous day but for some reason was pointedly sitting with Ethan between her and Denver. Once the music had finished, Keith made a phone call to somebody called Sol to give him the monumental news that Royalty were coming out of retirement. It was only as Steph listened to the conversation that she realised that Sol had to be Solomon Phoenix, the head of the music division at the biggest media company in the world. Ethan had even referred to him on occasions as 'God'. She could only hear Keith's side of the conversation, but it rapidly emerged that God wasn't going to wait for them to send him the finished article. He was coming to them.

After Keith broke the news to him that the group was re-forming, the great man was so enthusiastic he offered to come over to Italy in person to listen to the new material. Even Keith was taken aback despite, as Steph had told her mother before coming over here, Royalty re-forming being just about the biggest news of the year, if not the decade, for the music business. After putting down the phone, Keith explained to them that Solomon was a man who liked his food, and Italian food in particular, so he hadn't taken long to start making plans to jump in his private jet and head over from the States in a few days' time.

Keith gave Steph a little smile. 'I didn't tell him about our fabulous replacement keyboard player, so it'll be interesting to see what he says when he meets you, Steph.'

Steph gulped.

After dinner she left the family in the dining room and went back to her room. The rain had passed by now and although the path was still wet, she got back to her room safe and dry. After phoning her mum, she set about washing some clothes in the bathroom, and she was still in there when her phone started ringing. Her heart leapt as she saw the caller ID.

'Rob, hi.'

'*Ciao*, Steph, I hope I'm not disturbing you.' Wiping her hands on a towel, she sat down on the edge of the bed to talk to him.

'*Ciao*, Rob, of course not, I'm delighted to hear from you. All well? How's my four-legged friend? I haven't seen him today.'

'He sends his love. Thanks for your help and your company last night. It was a lovely evening.'

'I feel the same way. It was great. When are you off to Sanremo?'

'That's the thing; I'm off early on Saturday morning and I wanted to see you before I go, so I was wondering if you were busy tomorrow night?' Although the rational part of her brain immediately told her this would only prolong the agony by allowing her more time to fall under his spell, and that would just increase the hurt when she had to leave him and his dog behind, she felt an upsurge of excitement. She was about to reply eagerly when he hurried on. 'Would you maybe like to come out for dinner again? I promise I'll do my best to be cheerful and to keep you cheerful.'

'I'll hold you to that. I'd love to see you but there's no need for you to buy me more food.' A thought occurred to her. 'Tell me, do you like risotto?'

'I love a good risotto, but it's one dish I have great trouble making. It either ends up burnt and stuck to the bottom of the pan or a mushy inedible mess.'

'Right, well, you might remember me boasting about how my dad taught me to make real Venetian risotto. I'd be happy to come around to your place and cook for you. We could even play a bit first, if you like.' She was referring to music, but her subconscious could think of quite a few other ways they could play together, but she steadfastly refused to listen. For now.

'Only if you're sure. I'd happily take you anywhere you want.'

'Thanks for the thought, but I'd be very happy just with you and Waldorf in that gorgeous house of yours.' And, of course, there was no risk of paparazzi popping up there.

They arranged that she would come around the next day at six and she resolved to see Cesare at breakfast to see if she could scrounge a lift into town to buy the bits she would need. As the call ended, she lay back on the bed and stared up at the ceiling, her mood suddenly a lot lighter than it had been only minutes before. Might this mean progress in their fledgling relationship? Of course, she reminded herself, even if it did, there were still so many potential stumbling blocks, ranging from her future career to that blasted biopsy.

–

Steph got up early and hitched a lift into Lerici with Cesare first thing on Friday morning to buy the necessary ingredients for dinner and was back at the villa by half past nine just as the others assembled at the studio. Keith had some news for them.

'I woke up to find my work phone absolutely flooded with messages and emails. Sol must have been talking and the word has spread like wildfire.'

Steph was puzzled. 'Your *work* phone? You have two phones?'

'Absolutely, and I advise you to do the same. As soon as your name appears on the new album, you'll start getting pestered. And don't forget there'll be promotional videos that you'll be appearing in, so your face and ID will soon be out there, so it's best to be prepared in advance. Get a new phone: one for close friends and family and one for anything to do with work, whether it's the record company or the taxman. I keep that one permanently on *Mute* and, like I say, it's been working overtime while we've been sleeping.'

Johnny joined in. 'And get yourself another email address. The same applies to all social media. Otherwise, you'll never have a moment's peace.'

'Blimey.' Steph sat down on a nearby stool and realised, almost for the first time, how her life was about to change. Seeing the expression on her face, Ben offered encouragement.

'Or you can do what I've done for the last ten years: just cut yourself right off. I avoid social media like the plague and I can count on the fingers of one hand the people who have my phone number.' He caught her eye and she read sympathy in his. 'Like it or lump it, Steph, when the word gets out that Vince's place on the album has been taken by a woman, and that she's young and beautiful to boot, you'll have half the world's media snapping at your heels.'

'Blimey.' Aware that she was becoming repetitive, she thanked Ben for his kind words and resolved to heed his advice. As for the 'beautiful' comment, she took that with a pinch of salt. Like his colleagues, he spent most of his life wearing dark glasses. She looked around at the three of them. 'I'm going to need all the support and advice you can give me, so please don't hold back.'

Keith and the others felt that the first track they were working on this morning should start with a slow acoustic piano solo that would set the sober mood of the song and so she found herself directly involved in the creative process, trying out a mixture of chords, improvising, experimenting until she came up with a riff that gained universal approval. Even Ethan gave her a thumbs-up. As she played it over and over again until it was burned into her memory banks, she had to struggle to banish the thought from her mind that in a year's time this same piece of music might well be listened to by millions of people all over the world. It was a tantalising, but scary, thought.

When lunchtime came around, everybody filed out into the fresh air. The sky had now completely cleared once more, and it was hot again. Before she could follow the band members up to the villa, she felt a tap on her shoulder.

'Can you spare me a few moments, Steph?' It was Ethan and he was sounding unusually hesitant.

She turned and followed him back into the studio. 'What's up? Something not right? I thought it all went really well this morning.'

'Yeah, yeah, it was all good. You were great.' Clearly this was gentle, friendly Ethan today, rather than the bitter and twisted version who surfaced from time to time. What was clear, however, was that it was also a severely worried Ethan. 'Listen, Steph, I've got myself into a bit of a fix.'

'In what way?' She perched on a stool and took a closer look at him. He had been bright and businesslike all morning, but now his expression was far more insecure. 'What's happened?'

'It's Willow… She spent the night with me.'

Steph distinctly felt her jaw drop. 'She did what?'

'I've got to know her quite well since we've been here. I talked to her for hours at that club the other night while Den was off chatting to a load of other people. We got on really well together and she told me things weren't going so smoothly with Den. Then last night she had another row with him and turned up at my door in the middle of the night.'

'And you let her in?' Steph was aghast at the possible ramifications of this confession.

'Yeah, and she stayed the night.'

'In your bed…?'

He immediately looked up. 'Yes, but, listen, Steph, nothing happened between us. It's a big bed and she slept on one side, and I slept on the other. No contact, I promise. She just had nowhere to go, you see…'

Steph subjected him to her most searching stare but had to conclude that he appeared to be telling the truth. She gave a frustrated sigh. 'Oh, God, Ethan. And does Denver know where she spent the night?'

'I don't know. She got up and left early this morning not long after we heard your bedroom door close. I assume she went back to him, but I've no idea really.'

Steph's mind was racing. Ethan had just spent the night with his boss's son's girlfriend. Whether anything had happened was unimportant. When this all came out into the open, there was the very real risk that the result might be that Ethan might be expelled from the villa and, as his employee, she might even have to leave with him. Where this would leave the new Royalty album or her future career, remained to be seen, but she had a sinking feeling that Ethan might just have scuppered both of them.

She left him there to stew and went up to the villa. Now that the rain had passed, Cesare had set tables on the terrace once more and the three band members were already helping themselves at the buffet, no doubt keen to get back to work. Denver was sitting at a table on his own and there was no sign of Willow. Steph decided she had better speak to her, so she gave the band members a wave and went inside looking for Cesare or his wife and found Donatella in the kitchen.

'*Ciao*, Donatella. I need to speak to Willow, but she hasn't come down yet. Can you tell me which room's hers?'

'She's in Denver's room at the back of the house. You can't miss it. Go up the stairs, turn right and it's the last door at the end of the corridor.'

Steph thanked her and set off up the stairs to the first floor. When she reached the last room on the right, she tapped on the door. She had to knock twice more before Willow opened it. From the expression on her face, she had been crying.

'Willow, hi. Listen, we need to talk. Can I come in?'

'I don't see...'

But Steph had already pushed past her into the room. She stopped as she reached the bed and turned back to face the girl who was looking confused. 'I've been speaking to

Ethan. Do you feel like telling me what happened last night?'

Willow's face hardened. 'That's none of your business. Why don't you go off and leave me alone?'

Steph refused to be intimidated. 'Ethan said that nothing happened between the two of you and I believe him; not that it matters to me what did or didn't happen, because we've split up. What have you told Denver?' She held up an admonitory hand to stop Willow retorting. 'This is for your own good, honestly. I'm here to help.'

Willow made another couple of attempts to stand her ground before her shoulders slumped. 'I haven't told him anything. At least, I said I spent the night just wandering about or sitting on the beach. We had a major bust-up, you see. It's been building up for a few days.'

'So Ethan said. And did he believe you?'

'I don't know. He was pretty mad, and he stormed off before breakfast. I haven't seen him since.'

'What I need to know is what you intend to do. Do you want to stay with Denver, or what?'

By now Willow was looking more like a dejected teenager than a grown woman. 'I like Ethan, but just as a friend. I wasn't really thinking straight last night, or I wouldn't have gone to his room, but I couldn't think of anybody else. I like Den, but he gets crazy when he's on drugs.'

Steph took a couple of deep breaths. 'Well, if you want my advice you'll dump him or at the very least give him an ultimatum: you or the drugs. How did he get his hands on drugs? Did he bring them with him from the States?'

Willow shook her head. 'No, he met up with some guy when we were in Florence last week and got the stuff from him. That's why we went there.'

Steph remembered the way Denver had appeared unusually relaxed that evening and been kissing people. 'And he's the one who's been giving drugs to Ethan?' Seeing Willow nod, she did a bit of quick thinking and made a decision. 'Look, for now why don't you tell him you spent the night in my room? I'll back you up if he asks me. That way he can't accuse you or Ethan of anything. But then if I were you I'd distance myself from him. Is there anybody you know over here in Europe where you could go and stay?'

Willow nodded. 'I've got a friend who's staying not far from here. I expect I can go and stay there.'

'Great. Then get onto this friend and just go. Tell Denver he can call you when he's cleaned up his act and if he doesn't, you're better off without him. If you want, I'll drive you there myself in the minibus. Cesare said I could borrow it if I needed it.'

'Thank you but I'm sure my friend will come and pick me up.'

When she got back downstairs she spotted Ethan sitting alone at a table, so she went over to see him. She explained what had transpired between her and Willow and saw an expression of relief and considerable gratitude flood over his face.

'Steph, that's brilliant. Thanks so much. You got me out of a real hole, and I owe you, big time.'

'Well then, if you owe me, I want you to do something for me in return: give up all this drug nonsense. You don't need that sort of thing. Your life's good, your career's going great, and with your name going to be forever associated with Royalty, the sky's the limit for you and the company. If you really want to repay me, do us both a favour and get clean.'

Chapter 18

That evening Steph agonised over what to wear for her dinner date with Rob before deciding to keep things laid back and she settled on shorts and the T-shirt with his name and picture on it that she had bought at the concert in Fiesole as a souvenir. This should at least give him a laugh. After collecting the food Donatella had been keeping in the fridge for her, she set off down to the beach and up the path to Rob's house. As before, she was intercepted en route by the Labrador who gave her a boisterous welcome. When she got to the door and Rob appeared, she saw him take in the new T-shirt and grin.

'Now that's just plain mean. How am I supposed to keep my eyes on your face when all I see is my own face?'

'I hope you'll be far too busy keeping your eyes on the cookery lesson, Mr Bailey.' She adopted a schoolmistress tone. 'I expect my students to pay attention at all times.'

'Yes, miss.' He bowed with mock servility. 'Do come in, please.'

Once again she avoided kissing him, even on the cheeks, and just walked in past him. 'It's good to see you. Thanks for the invitation.'

Without waiting for him to respond she went through to the kitchen and unloaded her purchases onto the worktop, closely supervised by the dog and less covetously by his master. She was quick to tell him about the most important ingredient: 'I bought a new packet of Carnaroli rice just in case you didn't have any in the house. As it's the main ingredient, my dad always instilled into me that it has to be Carnaroli. No other rice will do for a real risotto.'

'I didn't know that. Maybe that's where I've been going wrong.' Rob appeared at her side and studied the food on the worktop. 'It looks like you've bought ham and salami as well. You didn't need to go to all this trouble.'

'It's hand-cut cured ham that the man at the shop in Lerici told me comes from his uncle's farm in the hills, and the sausage is *finocchiona*, which I love for the spicy fennel taste. There's focaccia and goat's cheese, and for dessert I just bought some pastries. I thought about having a go at making you my dad's very own tiramisù, but I would have had to start this morning so it could set in the fridge and we've been in the studio all day.'

'You shouldn't have…' He went over to the fridge and pulled out a bottle. 'I've got some of Donatella's uncle's homemade sparkling white. Feel like helping me drink it?'

'Useful things, uncles. Yes, thanks, I'd love a glass.'

Steph finished putting the ham and the other bits and pieces in the fridge while Rob opened the wine and filled two glasses. 'Here, to the chef!'

They clinked their glasses together and she took a sip of the wine. It was remarkably good. 'Mmh, yum. What time do you normally eat? I'll need ten minutes to sort out the antipasti, and then the risotto will take about twenty-five minutes or so.'

'Whatever suits you: eight, or earlier or later. You choose.'

'Eight's fine with me. So that gives us over an hour before we need to start preparing the food. What do you want to do? I'm very happy to accompany you on the piano if you feel like a bit more practice.'

He shook his head. 'Thanks, but you've been at the keyboard all day and you're cooking dinner so why don't we just go and sit outside and relax? After the rain the views are great.'

He led her outside to the loggia. This was a terrace attached to the house covered by a sloping roof and with open, arched sides overlooking the sea. Sheltered from the direct sunlight and with a gentle cooling breeze the temperature here was perfect. They sat down side by side on a wicker sofa with the dog sprawled on the old brick floor at their feet. They were little more than a few metres from a low wall that marked the edge of the cliff, and the views, as Rob had said, were spectacular.

Steph relaxed back onto the cushions and gradually they started to talk. They talked about all sorts of things, not just his and her music, and the conversation ebbed and flowed without any awkward pauses. She even ended up talking about her fears about the outcome of the biopsy and he was as supportive as his mother had been. As promised, he was communicative, cheerful and warm, and the hour flew by until a glance at her watch told her it was time to head for the kitchen.

While she pulled out the ham, *finocchiona* and bread and made nibbles for them to eat as she cooked, he refilled their glasses and watched as she talked him through the not too complicated business of making risotto.

'The first thing is to use a good, solid, flat-bottomed saucepan. And into that you put a little olive oil and a similar amount of butter. I know cooking with butter isn't big in Italy but Dad always told me it made all the difference to a good risotto. Begin by frying the chopped onions gently, but don't under any circumstances let them go brown. You just need to blanch them.'

While this was happening, she asked him to grate some Parmesan cheese to be added when the dish was finally served. He did as instructed, and then stood there looking on until she decided the time was right to tip in the rice.

'Gently stir the rice so it mixes with the onion and let it colour gradually. At this point the whole thing's very dry so pour in half a glass or even a full glass of white wine – I hope Donatella's uncle doesn't find out we've used his lovely wine for cooking – and then start adding occasional ladles of chicken stock as needed. I asked Donatella for a bag of stock from her freezer as I didn't have any. Why don't you continue stirring gently and adding stock until the rice is just about cooked? It's dead easy.'

She handed him the wooden spoon she had been using and watched as he did as he was told. Truth to be told, she enjoyed watching him, every bit as much as she did supervising his culinary ability. Finally, reluctantly, she tore her eyes off him and decided it was time for the next stage.

'Tonight, we're going to throw in a big handful of peas and a heap of chopped ham but you can use all sorts of ingredients from prawns to mushrooms or whatever takes your fancy. Keep tasting it until the rice reaches the consistency you prefer. Personally, I like it *al dente*. Whatever you do, don't let it cook too long and don't let it dry out. Then, when it's just about ready, squeeze in a clove of garlic and just let that mix briefly before taking the pan off the gas. Some people say you should fry the garlic along with the onion at the start, but Dad always said it was best added at the end so it doesn't run the risk of burning and tasting bitter.'

She took the pan across to the table and divided the risotto onto two plates. 'And that's all there is to it. Sprinkle it with the Parmesan and add a good twist or two of black pepper and it's ready. We can finish the antipasti with it or after it, but the risotto's best eaten hot. *Buon appetito.*'

He brought a bottle of red out of the fridge and drained the last of the sparkling wine in his glass. 'When the weather's as hot as it is today I keep the red wine in the fridge. Although it might make a few diehard wine buffs wince, I think it's the only way. Finish your white and try the red.'

The risotto was a great success – or at least that was what he said. As far as she could judge, he enjoyed it and she certainly enjoyed his company more than the food. The red wine from the fridge was very good and the atmosphere between them relaxed and, as he had promised, cheerful. From time to time she glanced across the table at him and knew that under other circumstances she could really have seen this developing into something special. As it was, with his concert tour starting tomorrow and her departure from Italy likely to be only a matter of days after he came back – plus the other big unknown of the biopsy – she knew she was on a hiding to nothing.

At the end of the meal, they went out into the loggia to eat the little pastries she had bought from the *pasticceria* in Lerici. These were a tasty mix of fruit tartlets and profiteroles with a variety of toppings and, accompanied by coffee from his machine, they were an excellent way of finishing off the meal. By now the light had faded and they were sitting side by side in almost complete darkness, and she couldn't help a feeling of delicious anticipation descending on her. In spite of her doubts about the future, she wanted to concentrate on the here and now and let the future look after itself. What was that old quotation about it being better to have loved and lost?

Alas, Rob didn't appear to be on the same wavelength. He was sounding more pragmatic than romantic. 'You say the big man's coming over from Hollywood next week?'

'Yes, at the end of the week, I believe.' She swallowed her coffee and, with it, a little wave of disappointment.

'By which time you hope to have all the tracks recorded?'

'Yes, in near final form. We'll still need backing singers and a few other instruments for some of the tracks like a sax and some bongos.'

'Assuming he likes what he hears, you could be off to the States or the UK as early as next weekend to produce the final version, and I wouldn't see you back over here again?'

'I'm afraid so.' Put like that, it was painfully clear that, nice as it might be to have a little fling with him here and now, that was all it could be: a fling. He was due back from his tour on Thursday and Solomon Phoenix was due to arrive the same day or at most the day after. That didn't give time for anything to develop, even if she decided to throw caution to the winds. Then, for just about the first time, he brought up the subject of relationships.

'I heard that you and Ethan are close. Is that right?'

'We used to be together, but that's all over now.' She came close to telling Rob that he had eclipsed Ethan in her heart but firmly kept a lid on it. What was the point, seeing as this was one of the last times they would see each other?

'I'm going to miss you.' He said it as she was gathering the courage to say the exact same thing.

'I'm going to miss you, too.' She reached over and caught hold of his hand. 'I've known you for such a short time, but it feels as if I've known you for ages.'

'The same here. I like you a lot, Steph.' And, to her delight, he leant towards her and kissed her softly on the cheek. 'An awful lot.' There was tenderness in his voice but there was also a note of regret. Clearly, he realised and accepted the situation. Seconds later, before she could say or do anything, he pulled himself to his feet. 'I think it's about time I took Waldorf for a walk.'

The dog was currently snoring happily with his heavy head on Steph's feet, but at the sound of the magic word he roused himself and leapt to his feet. Reluctantly accepting the wisdom of keeping Rob at arm's length, Steph followed suit and they set off. The sky was clear, and the stars illuminated the path as they walked through the woods. At first it was only wide enough for them to walk in single file behind the dog, but when it widened out she caught hold of Rob's arm with both of her hands and pressed her cheek against his shoulder.

'I can't think of anywhere I'd rather be or anybody I'd rather be with.'

'That's exactly the way I feel. Promise you won't forget me.'

'I could never forget you.' She pulled him to a halt and reached up to kiss him in her turn – just on the cheek and only for a second or two – but it felt so right, and her head was spinning as she stepped back. 'Besides, I've got this T-shirt now, so I'll always have that as a reminder.' It seemed like the best thing to make a joke of it. If not, she was afraid she might start crying.

They stood there, face to face. She could see the starlight reflecting in his eyes as they reached deep inside her. Seconds later, however, he stepped back, and she saw him glance at his watch.

'I've got an early start in the morning and you're going to be busy, so I'd better get you home.'

Repressing the wave of disappointment that swept over her, Steph shook her head. 'I can find my own way from here. You go on home. I'll be fine.'

'No, I'd like to. Please.'

They walked back through the trees and down the path to the beach where Waldorf was dissuaded by his master from taking a bath, before they climbed up to the studio. Here Rob slowed and turned towards her, taking hold of both her hands in his.

'It's been a wonderful evening. Thank you so much.'

'Thank you, Rob. I wish it didn't have to end so soon... all of it.' She knew what she meant even if he didn't.

'I know, it's a real pity but there's no other way, is there?'

'I don't know. Is there?'

He didn't answer. He just kissed her once again, only a chaste peck on the forehead, and then turned away. 'See you next week. And remember, don't forget me, Steph.' His voice sounded hoarse.

'That's something I could never do.'

Chapter 19

The next days passed in a flash. The weekend came and went and most of the time was spent in the studio, refining and improving the different songs until Ethan was able to record near final versions of each in readiness for the arrival of the record company boss at the end of the week. Every morning Steph checked her phone for a message from the hospital, but she waited in vain and with every day that passed, her apprehension grew.

Willow had taken her advice and left, followed on Saturday morning by Denver, who had flown off to the States in a huff. As a result, the atmosphere at table and in the lounge in the evenings had become far more relaxed. Denver's departure had a beneficial effect on Ethan as well, who appeared to have taken on board Steph's advice and was no longer looking the worse for wear. He was up early and in the studio on time every day, and in there he was back to his masterful self. What was interesting, however, was that even though he appeared to be transforming back into the Ethan she had fallen for in the past, she now felt no inclination to renew things with him. Somehow, getting to know Rob had shown her that she wanted more out of a relationship, even if it was clear that this wasn't likely to happen with Rob.

On Saturday night her life changed.

Keith, Ben and Johnny, looking unusually serious, sat down with her in the lounge before dinner and announced formally that they wanted her to join the band as the replacement for Vince and that they would like her to perform alongside them from now on. It became clear that they weren't just asking her to play with them, but actually to become a fully paid-up member of Royalty. She was quite overcome and came close to bursting into tears at the magnitude of this offer. She managed to keep a lid on it, but it was a close call. Keith gave her an encouraging pat on the arm.

'You're perfect, Steph. You play just like Vince and we four get on so well together.'

'Yes… but… this means I'd be a woman in an all-male band. Isn't that going to look weird?'

Ben was the first to respond. 'We weren't an all-male band by choice; that's just the way it worked out. But who cares about that anyway? The fact is that you're good and that's why we want you. Besides, it'll give the fans something else to look at apart from our wrinkles.'

'Well, if you're sure, I can't think of anything I'd love more.'

Keith gave her a satisfied smile. 'Excellent. Our old manager, Nick, disappeared years ago after the group split up, and our affairs have all been managed by the record company since then. I've already spoken to Hollywood and when Sol and his guys come over, they'll be bringing details of the financial offer with them next week. I told them to make sure it was something you wouldn't be able to refuse.'

Lottie, who had been sitting on the sofa watching approvingly, also offered some advice of a very practical nature. 'And before you go out on stage with these guys, come and have a long talk to me and the girls about clothes, particularly underwear. You wouldn't believe what the UV lights can show up.' She walked over and gave Steph a motherly pat on the arm. 'Between us, Faye and Tara and I will sort you out.'

As the days passed and Steph began to digest the magnitude of this amazing change to her life, she worked as hard as she could, memorising each of the numbers so that playing them became almost second nature. Ben, who was immensely supportive now that he had resumed his former place in the band, told her how vitally important this would become when the band went on tour. It was incredibly exciting and equally daunting, and Ben made sure she was aware of what awaited her.

'Here we are now in the studio. It's perfectly quiet apart from us, and there are no distractions. But imagine what it's going to be like when you're on stage, playing to a hundred thousand people in a football stadium at night. Apart from the pyrotechnics that we'll have going on behind us with a big screen, strobes and lasers, there'll be the spotlights that half blind you and then plunge you into darkness. There'll be guys carrying TV cameras sneaking about the stage, pointing them at you at close range. Add in dry ice that makes it hard to see your feet and the audience taking flash photos, shouting, screaming and singing along, and you get the picture: it's all too easy to freak out. Remember to keep your eyes and ears on the rest of us and on Johnny above all. He'll keep the beat and if you follow him you'll never go far wrong.'

The thought of playing to a hundred thousand people was seriously intimidating. Steph had been to her fair share of concerts and festivals but had never got anywhere near the action until the last couple of years, when working for

Ethan had taken her backstage and brought her into close contact with performers. Apart from the ones who had quite clearly already been drunk or stoned, almost every single artist she had seen, from virtual unknowns to world-famous stars, had looked awed at the prospect of going out on stage; like gladiators about to walk into the arena. Even scarier had been to see them come back off stage drenched in sweat and looking haggard after the physical and emotional strain of pleasing the baying crowd. She hoped she would be up to it when the time came.

She went for a swim most mornings and into the studio most evenings where she played Chopin and let her mind return to the man with the violin. Despite having known him for such a short time, she felt an acute sense of separation. The only upside to Rob's absence was that Waldorf was now a permanent resident at the villa and he often came swimming or for a walk with her and he even curled up happily beside the keyboard when she was playing. He must have sensed the conflicting emotions running through her as she alternated between euphoria at the thought of becoming a member of the band and the cold nagging fear in the pit of her stomach as to what the results from the hospital might bring. Somehow, Waldorf realised she needed his support and she found him at her side most of the time. At the table he stretched out across her feet to remind her he was there.

He really was a very good dog.

Things between her and Ethan had settled back into an uncomplicated working relationship and she found that she got on with him as well as ever, particularly now that he was behaving in a much more professional manner, just like he had been when she had first started working with him. Whether he realised that he had been eclipsed in her eyes by Rob was something they never discussed. If this occurred to him, he never commented, and he appeared quite happy dedicating himself to ensuring that he got the very best out of the band. She enjoyed working with him once more and she was happy for him.

The knowledge that she might only see Rob for another handful of days when he came back from his tour was hard to take. On Sunday evening Steph was with Faye and Keith in the lounge while the others were outside splashing about in the pool and they watched Rob on stage in Sanremo, performing to a packed house. Steph found herself humming along to the pieces, particularly the ones they had played together, although most of her attention was on the man himself. She also subjected his accompanist to close scrutiny. Apart from the fact that she played beautifully, Steph couldn't miss the fact that she was also a very attractive woman with a mass of glossy black hair. Doing her best to banish what was unmistakably a little pang of jealousy, she concentrated on the music. The last piece he played, in response to repeated cries of 'encore', was Massenet's exquisitely reflective *Méditation* that she had last heard him playing high up on the cliff top, and there were tears in the corners of her eyes by the time he came to the end of it. Finally, Faye flicked off the TV, glanced across and smiled.

'He does play very well, doesn't he?'

Steph nodded as she reached into her pocket for a tissue. 'He has such a sensitive touch.' Her voice must have betrayed her, and she felt Faye's eyes on her.

'He's going to miss you when you've gone.'

'Do you think so? I'll certainly miss him. It's crazy; I've only just met him, but he's made such an impression on me.'

'Well, if it helps, I think the same can be said for him and, for what it's worth, I'm delighted. He's been fooling around for so long now, he needed somebody like you to come along and shake him out of it.'

'And maybe I've been needing somebody like him to show me what I've been missing all these years.' Steph reached for the glass of very good cognac she had barely touched. 'Shame it's all going to end before it's even begun.' She took a sip but barely tasted it. 'He told me he's coming back on Thursday and the big boss man's coming the same day or the next, isn't he, and I suppose that'll be the end of any free time.'

Keith had been listening in to their conversation and he leant forward to offer her a top-up of cognac, which she refused with a smile and a little wave of the hand as he confirmed the arrangements. 'The latest I've heard is that Sol's flying into Pisa on Thursday. I'll send him over the demos if we can get them all recorded in time, but he'll want us to play the whole thing live to him. He's like that. He tells me he's putting their London studio at our disposal next week, so I imagine we'll be heading off there on Saturday or Sunday for the final recordings.'

Steph glanced across at his wife and shrugged. 'See what I mean? By the sound of it I won't even have a chance to say goodbye to Rob.'

Faye gave her a sympathetic smile. 'That's showbiz. Still, things can change. Just you wait and see.'

By the time Thursday arrived, Steph was in a state of heightened expectation as she awaited news of Rob's return and the arrival of the record company execs from Hollywood. Her excitement was tempered by the fact that nine days had now passed since her biopsy and so the result should be coming any minute now.

Rob hadn't told anybody what time he would be back, and she was half expecting to see him when she and Waldorf went down to the beach for their late afternoon swim, but there was no sign of him. She and the dog splashed around in the water for a while as she alternately threw a stick for him and floated lazily on her back in a reflective mood. Apart from the people she was going to miss when she left for London, she knew she would miss this wonderful private cove and the playful dog. For a moment she contemplated getting herself a dog but immediately realised that a dog, like a family and a settled home, was out of the question for the foreseeable future now that she had joined a rock band.

Her spirits received a boost later on as she emerged from the shower. Her phone bleeped and she saw that it was a text message from Rob.

> Hi, Steph. Hope all's well. On my way home. Fancy a late dinner? Say nine o'clock?

She answered straightaway.

> Sounds great. Call me when you get back. Really looking forward to seeing you again.
>
> x

The last thing she did before leaving her room was to check her emails but there was still no message from London. From what they had told her, news should arrive the very next day and she could only pray that it would be good news. Still, she told herself, she had dinner with Rob to look forward to, so she went up to the villa to tell Donatella that she wouldn't be having dinner with the family. When she got there she suddenly discovered that it wasn't going to be as simple as all that after all. Faye was sitting on the terrace enjoying the last of the evening sunshine and she had news.

'There was a call a couple of hours back. Sol's on his way. Keith and Cesare have gone off to Pisa airport to collect him and his people. They should be back here around nine and we all need to be on parade, so we've put off dinner until a bit later on. I hope that's okay with you.'

Steph groaned inwardly and Faye must have spotted something on her face. 'What is it? Something wrong?' Her expression became suddenly serious. 'Have you heard from the hospital?'

'No, nothing yet, but it's just that I've had a text from Rob asking me to meet him for dinner at nine.' Her brain was working overtime, trying to find a solution, but the inevitability of what she had to do gradually settled on her. 'I'd better give him a call and put him off.'

Faye gave her a sympathetic look. 'I'm afraid you don't have much choice. You're the new member of the band, after all, and Sol will be keen to meet you. Work's work…'

Steph tried to muster a smile, but it hurt. 'And so it begins.'

'But if you're talking to Rob, ask him to come and eat with us tonight.' Faye smiled. 'That way you'll at least have a chance to talk to him. And so will I.'

Steph collected the dog from the kitchen where he had been shadowing Donatella, and the two of them went for a walk in the woods surrounding the villa. When she reached a suitably deserted spot, she perched on a log and called Rob. He answered almost immediately and from the background noise she could tell he was in the car.

'Hi, Rob, it's me… Steph. Are you okay to talk?'

'Hi, Steph, yes of course. I'm on the autostrada near Genoa and the traffic's crawling along. I should hopefully still be home for nine. I'm really looking forward to seeing you.'

Steph took a deep breath. 'I'm afraid that's why I'm ringing.' She went on to tell him how his father and the others had offered her a place in the band and that the record company's big boss was descending on them that evening. 'I'd much rather be with you, but I suppose I really have to be here to meet this guy and his "people". You do understand, don't you?'

'Of course I understand and I'm delighted you're going to be in the band. Maybe we can meet up tomorrow. I'm home for a full week now before I go off to Prague.'

'Your mum told me to ask you to come up to the villa for dinner tonight. At least that way we get to see you. Denver and Willow have left, so it's a far better atmosphere now, although Solomon Phoenix and his team will be there too. It looks as though I might be leaving for London at some point this weekend and I'd really love to see as much of you as possible before I go. Please come.'

'I'll be there. Will you tell Mum and Donatella, please?'

Solomon Phoenix and his 'people' comprised one large man in his sixties and two immaculately turned-out men in their thirties. These two were introduced as Zach and Vic but there was no explanation of their different roles. Steph was feeling very nervous by the time they arrived, not least as Rob had not yet returned. When

Keith introduced her to Sol, she saw the big man's eyes light up.

'Steph, hi. It's great to see a woman in the band. Hey, Keith, good choice. The fans are gonna love you, Steph.'

'You wait till you hear her play, Sol. She's amazing!' Keith was looking and sounding far more animated than usual, and Steph exchanged glances with Ben. He had told her earlier to expect Keith to morph into a much more driven being when the big man arrived, and it looked like he was dead right. 'It's like having Vince back with us.'

'That's great but Vince, God bless him, never looked like Steph, did he, guys?' This was addressed to the two men in suits, who both nodded in unison.

'She looks great, Pop.' The first to answer was Zach, and Steph filed away the fact that this indicated he was Sol's son. Immediately afterwards, the other suit replied.

'Perfect. The more women the better these days.'

Steph began to feel slightly resentful of the way these men were discussing her as if she wasn't here. She came close to retorting that what counted was her ability to play the keyboards, but she managed to restrain herself. Apart from anything else, these were the people who had supposedly come to make her an offer she couldn't refuse. Further conjecture was interrupted by a cold wet nose nudging her thigh and a hand brushing her shoulder. She turned to see Rob and his dog standing there and she very nearly threw herself into his arms but the presence of Solomon and his team, not to mention her ex-boyfriend, restricted her to a beaming smile.

'Hi, Rob, welcome back.'

He gave her a smile in return and did the round of the room, shaking hands with Sol and the suits and kissing his mother on the cheeks, but he didn't kiss Steph. His father, still sounding very upbeat, greeted him with an invitation. 'Have you heard that Steph's going to join the band? We're performing all the new numbers tomorrow morning for Sol. Maybe you might feel like dropping by as well to listen to our new stuff. We'd all value your opinion.'

'Of course.' Rob sounded eager. 'I'm dying to hear what the new Royalty sounds like, particularly now it boasts a woman in the line-up.' He shot Steph a grin. 'I'll definitely be there.'

Donatella surpassed herself at dinner. As a starter she served lightly grilled scallops accompanied by homemade Russian salad and a tomato, mozzarella and basil salad. She followed this with homemade lasagne and then sumptuous cold lobster halves and massive T-bone steaks grilled by Cesare on the barbecue. Keith had dug out some wonderful wines from his cellar and Solomon went into raptures about everything. By the time they reached the exquisite panna cotta topped with caramelised wild blueberries, Steph was just about ready to burst, and a look around the table told her that they all had thoroughly enjoyed the meal.

For her part, the enjoyment wasn't just due to the excellent food. Rob had taken a seat beside her with his dog stretched over both sets of feet and they had talked almost nonstop. The first thing he had asked had been whether she had heard anything from the hospital and when she shook her head, he was quick to reassure her that bad news tended to travel faster than good. She shot him a grateful smile but knew she would continue to worry all the same. He told her all about the three different concerts he had done, and she told him about the progress the band had made with the new album and the time passed all too quickly. Every now and then she glanced across the table towards Ethan and was pleased to see his attention directed almost exclusively at the men from Hollywood. Any fears she might have been harbouring that her interest in Rob might have grated with him appeared to have been unfounded. It looked as though he had moved on, just as she had, and she was relieved to see it.

The Americans were weary after their transatlantic flight – albeit accomplished in the luxury of a private jet – and when they went off to bed Rob also got up and took his leave. Steph would dearly have liked to at least walk with him to his house but as he had the car here at the villa, she just waved goodbye to him and his dog and watched them drive off. Still, she told herself, tomorrow was Friday and in all likelihood she and the rest of the band would be leaving for London the following day, so it was probably just as well if she didn't get to spend much time with him as this would only increase the hurt when the final parting took place.

Chapter 20

The email from the hospital arrived just before eleven next morning and it couldn't have come at a worse time. Steph and the others were midway through their live performance of the new numbers under the watchful eyes and attentive ears of Sol and his team, with Faye, Lottie, Tara and Rob sitting at the back of the studio, looking on. Steph had been feeling scared stiff at the start but had gradually relaxed as she got into it. When the phone in her shorts pocket started to vibrate to announce the arrival of an email she was completely thrown for a few moments, and she could hardly wait for the end of the song so she could peek at the sender ID. When she saw who it was from she looked desperately across at Keith, but he was busy talking to Sol. She swung her head around and managed to catch Faye's eye. Whether it was intuition or sixth sense, Faye immediately realised what was happening and before Steph could say anything, Faye stood up.

'Would you guys mind if we take five? I urgently need to speak to Cesare, otherwise we won't have anything to eat for lunch. Besides, I could murder a coffee.'

Steph glimpsed a look of annoyance on Keith's face, which disappeared almost immediately as he must have read something in his wife's expression. He pulled off his headphones, set down his guitar and stood up. 'Good idea to take a little break. I need to stretch my legs. I'm not getting any younger.'

Sol grinned and stood up in his turn. 'Sounds good to me and I'd love another coffee, but before we all split up I just have to tell you guys that I'm loving what I'm hearing. Royalty is gonna go platinum yet again, I can feel it.' He glanced over at his 'people'. 'Am I right or am I right?'

'You're right.' The harmony was perfect and if Steph hadn't been so worried she could almost have laughed.

As it was, she headed for the door and ran down the path to the beach, pulling out her phone as she did so. She leant back against her favourite rock and opened the email, her hands sticky with nervous tension as she read it through. It was written in sober medical language, and she made a point of reading every word right up to the end. When she finally finished, she slowly and deliberately set the phone down on the rock beside her before bursting into a flood of tears which she was quite unable to staunch. Seconds later she heard the crunch of steps on the sand and felt a comforting arm stretch around her shoulders. She looked up to find Faye standing beside her with an expression of such compassion on her face, it only made her sob all the more. Mutely, she handed the phone to the former nurse to read while she did her best to regain some sort of control. Less than a minute later she received a hearty hug and a kiss on the cheek from Faye.

'See? I told you it would be fine. All good, *no further action required*. What more could you ask for?'

Steph nodded a few times, pulled out a tissue and blew her nose, wiped her eyes and finally regained the power of speech. 'Thank you, Faye. I'm sorry, I just flipped. It was the waiting...'

'I know, dear. The waiting's the worst. But at least you now know that you've got nothing to worry about. You can concentrate on enjoying the rest of your life.' She gave Steph another kiss on the cheek and stepped back. 'And now I'd better go and see the others. That invention of mine about lunch was all I could think of on the spur of the moment, but it was ridiculous. Donatella's been planning all the meals for days. Still, it did the trick and gave you a chance to read your email. Come up when you feel like it. By the way, is it all right with you if I tell the others it was good news? Lottie was only talking about you this morning.'

'Of course, and thank you again. Now I'd better give my mum a call. Tell Keith I'll be back as quickly as I can.'

'Take your time. He'll understand. We all will.'

A couple of minutes later, after an emotional talk with her mum, Steph was just putting her phone back in her pocket when she had another visitor – or two if she included the dog. It was Rob, and on his face was the broadest beaming smile. He came running across the sand towards her and to her surprise and delight he swept her into his arms and hugged her so tightly she almost stopped breathing for a few seconds. She was vaguely aware of the dog jumping up on his back legs to paw her thighs in solidarity. When Rob finally released his grip on her, he took hold of both her hands and looked down at her from close range, the smile still on his face.

'Mum just gave me the news. I'm so pleased. I've been worried for you.'

She wiped her eyes with the now very damp tissue and smiled back at him. 'I've been worried for me too, but it's all right. Thanks for your support.' She glanced down at the dog, who was pressed tightly against her leg. 'And thank you, Waldorf.' In spite of her resolve to keep Rob at arm's length, she couldn't help reaching up with her hands to pull him down until she could kiss him, properly, on the lips. It wasn't a long kiss, but she knew the memory of it would linger with her forever.

No sooner had she done so than her brain reminded her that she would be off to London in the next forty-eight hours and that would be that. As she transferred her attention to the Labrador to give herself time to recover, she reflected that although one hurdle might have been cleared, the other hurdle still remained that she was about to embark on a new career as a rock star and that would potentially take her all over the world and away from this man. But for now, she didn't care. She raised her eyes from the dog and saw Rob with an expression on his face that was hard to read – part surprise, part what might have been regret. He waved vaguely in the direction of his house on the cliff top.

'I'd better go. I'm taking Waldorf home for a snooze, so he doesn't get in Donatella's way as she gets lunch ready. I'll be back in a couple of minutes.' And he left.

Knowing she needed to get back to the studio, Steph made a very quick call to Sky to give her the good news while walking back. Inevitably, Sky asked how things were progressing with Rob and Steph ended up recounting what had just happened. 'I kissed him, I mean kissed him properly on the lips, and he ran away.'

'So...?' Sky sounded as if she was grinning on the other end of the line.

'So I presume it means I overstepped the mark. He just thinks of me as a friend, but I went and screwed things up.'

'Of course you didn't. Listen, Steph, there's something you need to understand about my brother. For years now he's been hooking up with a never-ending succession of women and earning himself a reputation as a Lothario. Of course he fancies you – any man would – but the very fact that he hasn't been hitting on you shows how serious about you he is.'

Steph had to stop and think about this. 'You're saying that the fact that he hasn't ripped my clothes off and ravished me is because he likes me too much?'

'Don't let's get carried away here. I don't think anybody ever accused him of ravishing anybody who didn't want to be ravished, but what I'm saying is that I'm sure as sure can be – and he's my little brother, remember, I know him well – that he's crazy about you.'

'Oh…' Steph wasn't often stumped for words, but nothing came readily to mind. Luckily, Sky was running late.

'Anyway, we'll talk again soon. I was due in a meeting five minutes ago, so I have to scoot, but remember what I said. I know I'm right. Now, *ciao*.'

Steph didn't have time to dwell on Sky's words any longer as she was also running late so she hurried back up the path to the villa. Less welcome news was waiting for her when she reached the terrace and helped herself to a much-needed double espresso. Solomon announced that he had booked dinner that evening in a restaurant just along the coast from here and everybody was invited. Faye whispered in Steph's ear that the place he had chosen was one of only a handful of Michelin-starred restaurants in the region and the food, while excellent, was what Keith described disparagingly as 'too fussy by half'. As far as Steph was concerned, the menu wasn't the problem, it was the fact that this effectively torpedoed her chances of spending what might well be her last evening alone with Rob before she was due to leave for the UK. A few seconds later she discovered that his mind had been running along the same lines.

'I suppose you'll have to go for dinner with your future boss tonight.' She turned to see that Rob had returned from his house and was at her shoulder. 'It's a real shame. I would have really liked to take you out one last time before you leave.'

She didn't know whether to kiss him again or take two steps backwards, so instead she just reached out and gave his hand a little squeeze. 'I was just thinking the same thing. I don't suppose you can think of any way we could get out of it, can you?' The fact that he appeared to want to spend time with her maybe supported his sister's hypothesis, but there was no way of telling unless she could get him on his own.

He shook his head sadly. 'I can't, I'm afraid. You need to be there. The only good news is that it looks as though I'm roped in as well, so at least we can sit together.' He sounded genuinely disappointed and she took heart, determined to manufacture some alone time with him.

'We'll definitely sit together tonight, but how about we meet up on the beach later on this afternoon at, say, five-ish for a swim and then maybe you can offer me a cup of tea at your place before we need to get ready for the big dinner?'

'It's a date.' He glanced over to where the others were already starting to move back down the path towards the studio where Ethan was waiting for the second part of the performance. 'As soon as you finish playing, I need to get off home, but I'll be waiting for you at five. By the way, I've loved the new songs and Dad's right: you really fill Vince's shoes perfectly.'

233

One positive result of her outpouring of emotion down on the beach was that Steph returned to her keyboard quite unworried by the presence of the music industry execs in the audience and found herself playing fluidly and easily. In particular the piano solo in the final number of the morning went like a dream and she felt sure she couldn't have played it better. She soon found out that Sol shared her view as he came marching across to her and caught her right hand in his and held it up like a prize fighter after a famous victory.

'Outstanding, Steph. Just great. Not only do you play beautifully, you play like Royalty.' He looked back over his shoulder. 'Keith, Ben, Johnny, you couldn't have found a better replacement for Vince. Steph's a star.' He turned to his son and his colleague. 'Get the lady signed up, guys. Royalty needs her. We need her.'

By the time lunch was served on the terrace, Steph was clutching a long and intricate contract, full of legalese jargon. Keith told her he would introduce her to an expert lawyer in London to check it through before she signed on the dotted line, but all that Steph could do was to grin gormlessly and nod her head. She was still struggling to come to terms with the astronomical sums of money that looked likely to be coming her way from now on. Never in her wildest dreams had she ever believed something like this could happen to her.

With some apprehension she went to Ethan to break the news to him that she would definitely be leaving and was relieved to find him in a good mood. He accepted her immediate departure from his employment without a murmur and he even wished her well. He then went on to reveal why he was feeling so magnanimous: Sol and Keith had just told him they intended to employ him to finish the recording of the new album in London, but more importantly had offered him the position of tour manager when the big worldwide promotional push began early in the new year. By the sound of it, this would make him a lot of money, but it would, above all, elevate him to the very top of his profession. What was particularly interesting was the condition Keith had attached to the job offer.

'He told me he'd only employ me if I promised to cut down on the booze and stay off the drugs.'

'And you promised?'

'I did, and I meant it.'

'That's great. Just make sure you keep your promise.'

'I will.' Suddenly remembering, he went on. 'Wasn't today the day you were getting the results of your biopsy?'

She nodded and gave him the good news, pleased he had remembered. He then went on to demonstrate that he hadn't just been concentrating on his work. 'Have you told Rob? I bet he's happy for you. By the way, good luck with that. Long distance relationships aren't easy.' He sounded as if he meant it and she gave his arm a little squeeze.

'Thanks, Ethan.'

The lunch was outstanding once more, but Steph barely tasted it and spent most of the afternoon in a sort of daze. Now that the email from the hospital had removed the sword of Damocles from above her head, she could relax as she listened to Sol and his boys outlining the company's plans to promote the new album. This would involve making videos, issuing press releases, appearing on chat shows on both sides of the Atlantic, as well as a series of concerts in capital cities all around the world starting as early as December in London and followed by Sydney and Singapore in January. The album itself would be coming out at the beginning of December, to coincide with the inaugural concert and in time for Christmas, and Sol was already predicting mega sales. Finally, he announced that he would be taking the band members over to London the following day in his private jet. While excited at the prospect of a flight in a private plane, Steph couldn't help a sharp stab of regret at the thought that this would take her away from Rob.

The meeting broke up at four and they all went back to the terrace for tea and cake. As soon as she decently could, Steph excused herself and hurried back to her room. After giving her mum another quick call to tell her about the deal the record company was offering, she changed into her bikini, picked up a towel and her bag and went down to the beach to find the Labrador and his master waiting for her. She dumped her bag and towel on the rock and went over to greet both of them. First she stroked the dog and then she kissed his master, just managing to restrain the impulse to go for his lips again and picking his cheek instead. Still, it felt good, not least as both of them were nearly naked and the touch of him against her bare body felt amazing.

He stepped back as before but this time he gave her an admiring look. 'You were great today, you know. Particularly in the second half of the performance it was as if you'd developed wings and started soaring like a bird. You had a smooth fluidity of touch that even Anna Maria, my accompanist, struggles to maintain. Simply lovely.' His eyes ran up and down her body, giving her a little thrill, but then he turned and picked up the stick his dog had dropped at his feet. He lobbed it into the water and set off after it. 'Coming in? The water's perfect.'

Steph would happily have stayed on the beach with him, but she followed him into the water as bidden and found it wonderfully refreshing after the stresses of the day. She swam slowly after him and his dog and joined in a game of catch involving a stick while the Labrador paddled enthusiastically back and forth between them. After ten minutes or so they returned to the beach, and she dabbed herself dry with her towel, which had warmed up wonderfully on the sun-scorched rock. She picked up her bag and followed Rob and his dog up the narrow path to his house, and as she walked in, acutely conscious that all she was wearing was a bikini, she could feel a sensation of delicious anticipation building inside her.

It turned out to be misplaced.

They had only just settled down side by side on the wicker sofa under the loggia when her phone started ringing. Silently cursing the impulse that had made her bring it, she gave Rob an apologetic shrug and pulled it out of her bag. It was Ethan.

'Hi, Steph, you're needed. Sol's got a journalist and a photographer from *Hello!* magazine for an interview. They've just arrived now. You're big news, so you need to get back here pronto.' He lowered his voice. 'Best make it snappy. Keith's pacing up and down already.'

Her heart sank. First, there was a sense of trepidation at the upcoming interview along with the realisation that the photos would in all probability be seen all over the world, but even worse than this was the fact that it effectively knocked any chance of alone time with Rob on the head. Reluctantly she told Ethan she was on her way and rang off. As her eyes met Rob's she read understanding in them.

'Got to go?'

She shook her head ruefully. 'I really wanted to spend some quality time with you, but it seems *Hello!* magazine has decreed that it's not to be.'

'Well, at least we can sit next to each other tonight...' He looked as disappointed as she felt, but he rallied. 'Now, you'd better go. Solomon's not the sort of guy who likes to be kept waiting.'

They both stood up and there was an awkward moment while she considered kissing him properly for one last time, but he made no move so she chickened out and just gave him a helpless wave. 'I'm really sorry, Rob. See you later. Wish me luck.'

'You don't need it. You'll do fine. Now hop it, or your new boss will tell you off.'

She left him standing there with his dog and hurried back along the path and down onto the beach. If she hadn't been so preoccupied with her thoughts, she might have realised sooner who the two strangers on the beach with Zach and Vic were and what they intended to do. As she neared them she saw the man with the ponytail train an expensive-looking camera on her and she heard the whirr of repeat photos being taken. Too late she realised that she was still only wearing her bikini and by the time she had started to unroll her towel and wrap it around her body he had fired off multiple shots. The woman alongside the photographer gave her a big smile.

'Hi, Stephanie, I'm Gayle and this is Mikey. We're from *Hello!* magazine. It's great to meet you.'

Steph shook them both by the hand and answered a volley of questions before waving weakly at her dishevelled state. 'I'd better go up to my room and get changed. Can you give me a few minutes?' Before they could object, she sprinted off up the path and locked herself in her room, muttering, 'Bugger, bugger, bugger,' under her breath.

Luckily she had managed to keep her hair pretty dry while in the sea, but she barely had time to run a brush through it when she came out of the shower before she heard knocking at the door. It was Sol's son, Zach, urging her to get a move on. Still muttering an increasingly colourful string of expletives, she dressed as quickly as possible, deciding to wear the new blue and white striped dress she had bought in Lerici. She took a last despairing look in the mirror, threw the door open, and followed Zach down to the studio where the rest of the band had assembled.

'Ah, good, here you are, Steph.' Keith looked relieved. 'Come in. These guys want to talk to us and to take a few photos.'

Steph took a seat on a stool between Johnny and Ben and then more photos followed, of them all together, as well as separately, and almost an hour of questions about the band, the new songs, what had made them consider getting back together and, of course, Steph. Keith fielded most of the general questions. He appeared to be loving the media attention after so many years in the wilderness, and Steph intercepted winks from Ben from time to time as he and Johnny hardly got a word in edgewise. But then the attention turned to her, and she had to endure a barrage of questions about everything from her family – especially her father – to her music studies to how she had met Keith and the others. In among these questions were a host of more trivial queries like her favourite food, her favourite colour, where she bought her clothes – underwear from Marks and Spencer raised a few eyebrows

– and even the name of Snowball, the family cat. By the time the interview was over she was a wreck.

They all made their way up to the terrace as the light faded, and she willingly accepted a glass of champagne. Resisting the impulse to gulp it down in one, she took a small sip and looked across at Ethan who was being equally sparing, deep in conversation with Sol's 'boys'. She gave him a smile, but he was too engrossed to notice. A moment later she felt a hand on her shoulder.

'Faye told us the news. We couldn't be happier for you; about you joining the band, but the good news about your health is the most important thing.' It was Lottie and alongside her was Tara. They both hugged Steph warmly, but then Lottie said something that raised Steph's eyebrows.

'Ben and I are so pleased to see you with Rob. He's a lovely man and we think you're made for each other.'

'Made for each other?' Steph had never felt so bewildered. 'We're just friends…'

'Of course, dear, if you say so.' Lottie gave Tara a knowing wink and both women erupted into fits of giggling as they headed off.

Steph's embarrassment only increased as another hand touched her arm. '"Made for each other", eh?' It was Rob.

Steph jumped as if she had been stung and turned towards him. He had changed into a beautiful faded pink linen shirt, and he looked even more desirable than normal. Feeling her cheeks turn a distinctly brighter shade of pink than his shirt, she was quick to try to explain.

'You don't want to listen to them. They're just having fun. I promise I wasn't talking about you. Really…'

He reached out and took hold of one of her hands in his. 'How disappointing.'

'Okay everybody, our transport's arrived. Time to go.' Keith came striding across the terrace and caught hold of Steph by the arm. 'Steph, we're riding in the limo with Sol and Zach. All right?'

'Yes, of course.' This time Steph upended her glass of champagne and drained the lot before giving Rob a despairing look and allowing herself to be led away.

Chapter 21

The restaurant was just on the other side of Lerici, on the ground floor of a beautiful villa set in its own parkland overlooking the gulf. As the limo delivered them to the door, Steph surveyed the line-up of luxury cars parked outside. The total value of the cars on display was likely to be in the millions. She had another premonition – this time unrelated to her health – that this was likely to be her life from now on and she wasn't sure how much she was going to like it. Suddenly her simple cotton dress and M&S knickers began to feel distinctly out of place, as did she. She caught hold of Johnny's arm and shot him a pleading look.

'This is way out of my comfort zone. Promise me you'll keep an eye on me in case I do something stupid. I feel like a fish out of water.'

He grinned at her and gave her a reassuring pat on the hand. 'Tell me about it! I used to feel the exact same way. If it helps, I haven't been to a place like this for years. Of course we'll look after you, but I know you'll do just fine. Besides, I get the impression Keith's happy to do the talking for all of us.' His grin broadened and he gave her a wink just like his wife had done. 'And his son should be able to keep an eye on you.'

Immaculate waiters in pristine white jackets trimmed with gold braid led them through a marble-tiled hallway and into a huge dining room. The ceiling was covered by a vast mural of nymphs and shepherds and Steph's first impression was of walking into one of the historic palazzi her father had shown her in Venice. At the thought of her father, she wondered what he would have made of her sudden change in lifestyle. She knew he would have been happy at her success, but she also knew, deep down, that he had always wanted her to make it big in the world of classical, rather than modern, music. As she looked around at all the glitz and glitter, she had a feeling he was probably right. But she had made her bed, and now she had to lie in it. They were guided to a large table with twelve chairs close by French windows that opened onto the garden and the view. A light breeze came wafting through and Steph was grateful for it as she struggled to calm her nerves. A tap on her arm helped a lot. She turned to see Rob standing at her side and she immediately grabbed his hand.

'Am I glad to see you! Please promise me you'll stay by my side. I'm feeling a bit overwhelmed.'

'I'll stick by you like glue, that's a promise.' He gave her hand a squeeze and looked around the room. 'A senator, a couple of B-movie actors, a selection of the good, the bad, and the ugly, and a couple of high-class call girls. Pretty average for a place like this.' He grinned at her. 'But now, of course, they've got Royalty. Prepare for a lot of bowing and scraping.'

Seconds later the proprietor himself arrived, accompanied by the maître d' and a pair of waiters carrying trays of champagne. In excellent English the owner welcomed them and indicated that the champagne was with the compliments of the house, although Steph had a feeling he would recoup the cost of the wine many times over when Sol's people paid the bill at the end. Places like this were the ones that appeared on TripAdvisor with multiple pound signs alongside them – definitely not budget eating but, of course, it sounded as though her days of budget eating were over.

They started with a selection of antipasti that varied from the excessive to the indescribable. Along with langoustines, oysters, lobster tails and mussels in cream sauce, there was squid cooked in its own ink with liquorice and a lurid green concoction not dissimilar in appearance to mushy peas that looked as if it contained little worms or grubs. Steph missed the name of this alleged delicacy and only accepted a tiny portion from the waitress, which she then assiduously buried beneath empty mussel and crustacean shells. On her last night with Rob the last thing she wanted was to start throwing up at the dinner table.

She had Sol's son, Zach, on the left of her and Rob on her right. Although she would have loved to spend all evening just talking to Rob, she felt she had to divide her time between both men and Sol himself, who was sitting directly opposite her beside Keith who, as predicted, kept up a constant babble of conversation. She heard a lot more from Sol and Zach about the way they were planning to publicise the fact that Royalty were once more back together and how they were going to promote the new album.

Sol announced that as soon as they finished recording the final version in London they would be flown off to the USA for a series of TV interviews all over the continent, including Mexico and Canada. Although this all sounded exciting – if daunting – Steph knew it also signified that she was likely to be out of Europe for most of October which, of course, meant she wouldn't see Rob for ages. At the same time, Rob told her about his upcoming tours of Eastern Europe and Germany, and it appeared that he would be away almost as much as she would. This only underlined the impossibility of a relationship between them having a hope of developing, and she sighed inwardly.

She had just started on a plate of spaghetti laced with fennel, clams and roast scallops when her attention was drawn to some new arrivals. Through the door came an unlikely trio. First was the unmistakable figure of Cody Havergill, shadowed by his bulky bodyguard, as ever in his suit, and beside him was none other than Willow, dressed like a Hollywood vamp in a long silver dress.

'Cody! Is that you?' All heads turned as Solomon jumped to his feet and, accompanied by Vic and Zach, made his way over to greet the legendary rocker. Meanwhile, back on the Royalty table, the conversation very quickly turned to Willow.

'Wow, she didn't waste any time.' Tara looked as amazed as Steph was feeling.

'For God's sake, she's half, a third his age...' Faye looked equally gobsmacked.

Steph heard Rob's voice whispering in her ear. 'Say what you like; she's better off with Cody than with my brother... any woman would be.'

Steph gave him a nod in return. 'You're right, but I still think she could have chosen somebody a bit more suitable.'

'Rich, famous and by the look of him not long for this earth.' Rob was grinning. 'For my money he's exactly what she's been looking for.'

When Willow caught sight of Steph, she gave a little wave to which Steph replied. At least they had parted on reasonable terms, and the woman no longer appeared to be after Steph's blood. Sol and his 'boys' returned to the table and the meal continued. After roast duck in a chestnut, ginger and mandarin orange sauce, Steph excused herself and went to the Ladies. She was standing by a basin, dabbing cold water on her temples to try to cool down, when the door opened, and Willow came in. She came straight across and, to Steph's surprise, kissed her on the cheek.

'Hi, Steph, it's good to see you.'

'It's good to see you, too, Willow. Am I right in assuming that Cody's the friend you're staying with?'

Willow nodded. 'Yes, and he's great. He eats far too much and drinks as much as Den did, if not more, but he doesn't do drugs and he never turns nasty.' She glanced over her shoulder to check they were alone and grinned. 'He just falls asleep.'

While this sounded like a definite improvement on Denver, Steph reflected that this still didn't exactly sound like a match made in heaven by any means. But that was Willow's affair, not hers.

'Well, I'm glad if you're happy.'

'Listen, Steph, I owe you. You did me a big favour by offering to tell Den I spent the night with you rather than Ethan, so I think it's only right I should repay my debt. Now that you've broken up with Ethan, are you interested in Robert?'

'Um, sort of, but I'm leaving tomorrow, and I don't know when or if I'll see him again, so nothing's happened and nothing's likely to happen. Why do you ask?'

Willow looked reassured. 'That's good... not that you're leaving, but that things aren't getting serious between you and Robert. You see, I saw him last week. Cody took me to Monte Carlo for the weekend and we stopped off for a late meal on Sunday night in Sanremo on the way back. Robert was there in the restaurant with a very beautiful woman, and they were holding hands and all sorts. I thought you should know.'

The air hissed out of Steph's lungs. 'He was with another woman? Did he see you?'

Willow shook her head. 'I'm not sure, I don't think so. It was a big restaurant with two or three dining rooms, and we were in a different one from them. Besides, Cody insisted on sitting in the far corner – he doesn't like fans disturbing him when he's eating – and I just glimpsed Robert and the woman as we walked past the entrance to their room. I'm sorry, Steph, but when I saw you tonight I thought I should let you know.'

'Thanks…' Steph was genuinely amazed. She had really believed that Rob was a reformed character, but it was looking as though this particular leopard might not have changed his spots after all. Of course, it could all be innocent and above board, depending on what had been going on. 'When you say they were holding hands and all sorts, what kind of all sorts?'

'He was sitting opposite her, holding both her hands and looking deep into her eyes. He was just starting to kiss her fingers when I lost sight of him.'

'I see…' Steph took a deep breath and pulled herself together. So what if he'd been with another woman? Tomorrow would see her separated from him, probably forever, so it didn't matter, did it? She managed to muster a little smile for Willow's benefit. 'Out of interest, what did she look like, this woman?'

'She had a mass of jet-black hair and she was wearing a rather fine black gown, although it was a bit too conservative for my tastes.' Considering Willow's current dress was open to the waist, Steph could believe it.

Her antennae started bristling. That sounded very much like Rob's accompanist, and it didn't come as a complete surprise. Spending so much time together it was almost inevitable that they would have grown close. Swallowing her displeasure, she did her best to put on a bold front. 'Sounds like it's just as well nothing's happened between me and him. Thanks again for telling me.'

Pulling herself together, she returned to the dinner table and did her best to act as if nothing had happened. Rob was still charming and attentive, and Sol and his boys were still exuding a tsunami of confidence for the future of Royalty. Any gaps in the conversation were immediately filled by Keith, who was still firing on all cylinders. She smiled and responded from time to time while her brain continued to process what Willow had told her.

Of course, it might be a pack of lies. Maybe Willow had never forgiven her, and she had made this up as a way of getting payback for Steph's imagined interest in her original boyfriend. Besides, Rob's dinner companion might not have been his accompanist after all. Without seeing her, this was just supposition. She could have been a relative or a very close friend of his, although the black hair and gown were suspicious and the finger kissing was a bit intimate. It did of course sound very much like Rob's behaviour in his former, licentious incarnation. The finger kissing made what she had thought of as a special moment when he had kissed *her* hand feel somehow cheapened as a result.

She gave a little internal sigh. The most likely answer to this conundrum was that he hadn't really changed at all, and he was still an inveterate womaniser. Still, considering that after tomorrow she wouldn't see him again until his sister's wedding in December, it probably didn't matter. Actually, she told herself, knowing that he hadn't changed should make their separation all the easier to bear. She repeated this to herself over and over again, but it didn't help very much. In fact, it didn't help at all.

In consequence she was in a deflated mood when they returned to the villa. She joined the others on the terrace for coffee, but her head was elsewhere. It soon emerged that her hostess knew her well enough by now to smell a rat.

'How're you doing, Steph?' Faye appeared alongside her and caught hold of her hand. 'Feeling a bit overawed? Sol's like that but don't worry; Keith and the others will look after you.'

Very conscious that Rob was on the other side of her, Steph did her best to sound positive as she replied. 'Thanks, Faye. I'm sure it'll all be fine, and I know Keith and the others will keep an eye on me.'

'You'll soon get used to it. The rock world's a funny business with its ups and downs but you'll grow to love it.'

Steph nodded and heard Rob add his reassurance. 'You'll be great. In a few weeks' time you'll be so famous you won't want to talk to ordinary mortals like me.'

'You, an ordinary mortal?' Steph turned towards him and looked him in the eye. 'I imagine your fans, particularly your female fans, wouldn't agree.' For a moment she thought she saw something in his expression, but it might have been her imagination. Anyway, she told herself firmly, there was no point in causing a scene on her last night in his parents' house, so she turned back to his mother.

'I think it's time I had that talk about clothes with you and Tara and Lottie. I've got a lot to learn.' And, leaving Rob behind on his own, she let herself be led across to where the other ladies were standing.

The party broke up at midnight, and as everybody started going off to bed, Steph felt a hand on her arm.

'I need to give Waldorf a walk. He's been locked up all evening. Feel like coming with me?'

She came very close to saying no, but it was the chance of seeing the dog for one last time that swung it for her and she agreed, but she didn't catch hold of his arm as they walked down to the beach and up to his house. When they got there and Rob opened the door the Labrador came running out to greet them. They took him for a slow walk through the trees until they emerged near the cliff top, looking south towards the lights of the Tuscan coast. When they were close to the edge of the cliff, Rob stopped and turned towards her.

'I'm sorry you have to go.'

At that moment the dog returned and positioned himself between them. Steph bent down to ruffle his ears as she replied honestly. 'I'm sorry too.'

'This is going to be an exciting time for you, but please don't forget me.'

'Are you sure you won't forget *me*?' She came close to asking him about the woman in Sanremo but stopped herself in time. There was no point. Tomorrow she would be off.

'Impossible.'

They strolled back to his house and when they approached it she wondered if he was going to invite her in for coffee or more. She was mildly surprised when he just kept walking and accompanied her back to her apartment.

Not a word had been spoken since his promise never to forget her. Angel or demon, she knew she would never be able to forget him. He stopped at the entrance, and she saw the moonlight reflecting in his eyes. He made no move to draw nearer. Instead, he just stood there silently until she managed to find the strength to reach out and catch hold of him by the shoulders and kiss him gently on the cheeks.

'I won't forget you.' She stooped to pet the dog one more time and then opened the door. '*Ciao*, Waldorf, *ciao*, Rob.'

'*Arrivederci*, Steph.'

We'll meet again. But was that what she wanted?

Chapter 22

The next week passed far quicker than Steph could have imagined. The flight back to London in the luxurious private jet was an exciting experience; the contrast with her recent flights in crowded, utilitarian aircraft, striking. The days that followed were mainly spent in what appeared on the outside to be little more than a warehouse in East London, but which inside had been transformed into a state-of-the-art recording studio. In the course of nine days of hard work they managed to produce the final versions of all the songs under the watchful eye of Ethan and the increasingly strident interventions of Keith, who was beginning to revert to his original authoritarian persona about which Ben had warned her. She hoped he would calm down when the recording finished as she could see that his bossiness was already beginning to wear thin with both Ben and Johnny.

Making the album was a massive undertaking. For two of the tracks they had a twenty-piece orchestra playing along with them, on another a pair of amazingly talented bongo drummers, and on yet another an outstanding saxophone player flown over from New Orleans specially for the occasion. An equally talented trio of female singers provided backing on all but a couple of tracks and greatly enhanced the overall sound. The general opinion among the dozen or so employees at the studio was that the new album had all the makings of becoming a blockbuster.

Although the others stayed at a luxurious central London hotel, Steph opted to stay with her mum, conscious that she would be jetting off to the other side of the Atlantic very soon. She and her mum talked a lot and Steph recounted in detail how life had been at the villa. Needless to say, Rob's name came up and Steph ended up telling her mother about the anticlimactic way things had ended between them and what Willow claimed to have observed in Sanremo. Her mum listened intently before passing judgement.

'I'm very glad you didn't blow your top and have a scene. I've got a good feeling about this man, even if you haven't. So he was with a woman... that doesn't mean anything. Maybe it was his beautiful accompanist like you say, but that proves nothing. You've been spending every daylight hour recently with a bunch of men, but that doesn't mean anything's going on between you and any of them. Just you wait. When are you seeing him next?'

'That's the thing. Any day now we're off to America and it looks as though I'm likely to be over there for most of October. There's talk of making at least one promotional video – maybe more – and Keith says the company could choose to shoot the videos anywhere from Acapulco to Alaska. Realistically, I would think the first chance I'll have of seeing Rob again will be at his sister's wedding in mid-December.'

'And have you been talking, messaging each other?'

Steph shook her head. 'I haven't contacted him, and I haven't heard a thing from him.'

'Why don't you send him a message? Ask him how the dog is or something?'

But Steph just shook her head. 'I think it's best if we leave it like this. If Willow was telling the truth, it looks as though he hasn't changed, and I want nothing to do with a man like him. If there's an innocent explanation, he can give it to me at the wedding.'

'But at the wedding you'll be once again in the position of not wanting to make a scene. Shouldn't you do something about that now?'

'To be honest, Mum, I've got enough on my plate at the moment.'

Just exactly what she had on her plate became apparent a few days later when she got to the studio. Zach, left in charge by his father who had returned to LA, was waiting for her with Keith. There were broad smiles on both their faces and a pile of magazines on the table beside them. Keith was the first to speak.

'Hi, Steph, take a look. It's the latest edition of *Hello!* magazine and look who's on the front cover.' He sounded positively bubbly.

Steph took a copy from him, and her blood froze. The front cover was taken up almost entirely by a photo of the band, including her, with the headline: *Royalty Reform After Ten Years!* It was a decent photo, taken in the studio at Keith's villa, and everybody – herself included – looked good. Much less welcome was the photo that occupied the bottom right-hand quarter of the cover with the title: *Meet the New Royal.* The title wasn't the problem; it was the fact that the photo was of her in her damp bikini. Hurriedly she flicked through the inside pages and found no fewer than six full pages devoted to the news that the group were back together again, that they had a new album about to come out, and, in particular, that they had added a woman to the group. Five of the ten glossy photos were of her, and the captions ranged from the factual *Steph Zanin (29): first female member of the supergroup* to the more hyperbolic *Gorgeous replacement for tragic keyboard player* and even the contentious *Beauty among the Beasts*, alongside a selection of archive shots of scenes of the band's former misbehaviour.

'Pretty great, eh?' There was no doubt what Zach thought of the coverage. 'And now that the news is out there you bet the rest of the media will be getting very excited.'

The extent of the media excitement was brought home to Steph next morning when she went down to catch the tube across London to the studio. As she stood waiting for her train she couldn't miss a series of massive posters plastered on the wall in front of her consisting of a photo of the group and the words *BACK TOGETHER AGAIN* printed across them. Far worse, however, when she walked out of the station she passed a newsstand and saw that not only had the tabloids got hold of the story and were splashing it all over the front pages, some of them had also somehow got hold of the bikini photos and there was more of her naked flesh on display than she had ever thought possible.

This morning Zach's beaming smile stretched from ear to ear. He looked positively triumphant.

'Look, Steph, even the *Financial Times* has got the story on the front page and Pop tells me the news has spread across to the States with most of the papers running it in a few hours' time. How does it feel to be famous?'

Steph took another look at the photos of herself in what looked like an ever-smaller bikini – had it been Photoshopped? – and she shuddered. 'Oh, God...'

Zach didn't appear to notice her reluctance as he counted off on the fingers of one hand what they had coming up. 'Sky News at eleven, BBC at twelve thirty, ITV at two and Channel Four and a couple of others right after that. Then this evening there'll be some of the US media sources along with a selection of popular podcasts. Yup, it's all going great. Today's Tuesday, so that means we only have two more days here and then we fly over to LA. The company's throwing a big party on Friday night to celebrate. All the great and good of the music business will be there. You'll love it.'

Steph had a feeling she wasn't going to enjoy it as much as he predicted.

He went off humming happily to himself, and Steph slumped down on a chair and took a couple of deep breaths. She couldn't say she hadn't been warned. If she had had any doubts about how irrevocably her life would change, these had now been well and truly extinguished. Not only her name but also her body were in the public domain, and she would have to learn how to deal with it.

But it wasn't going to be easy.

The rest of the day was febrile. Somehow word must have gone out that she and the band were recording in the London studio and, as they left mid-morning for the first of the TV interviews, they found reporters and photographers crowding around the door outside. Staff from the studio had to come out and push intrusive journalists out of the way so she and the others could climb into the cars and set off. As they drove away, Steph's ears were still ringing to the shouts of 'Steph, Steph' that had been thrown at her from all sides. She felt a hand on her arm. It was Ben.

'I think this is what's called a baptism of fire. I'm afraid you'll find it a bit of a struggle at first, but you'll soon get used to it. Just remember that it's the novelty they like – the group getting back together and, of course, the new girl. In a few weeks it'll all calm down, don't you worry.'

'In a few *weeks*!' Steph groaned. 'Please, can you do me a favour? Stick by me at these interviews and if you think I'm making a fool of myself, just give me a kick, would you?'

She didn't get back to her mum's house until past nine that evening and she arrived feeling exhausted. She found her mother glued to the TV and received barely a wave from her. 'Come in and watch the news. They've been talking about you and the band all day. I've been getting phone calls from people I haven't heard from in years – old neighbours, some of your school friends and at least three boys who say they used to go out with you.'

Steph slumped down on the settee alongside the old white cat and gave a heartfelt sigh. 'What a day. It's all right for you, Snowball, just lazing about here at home without a care in the world.'

At that moment her phone bleeped, and she saw that it was a WhatsApp message. Suspicious that this might be somebody unwelcome who had seen her face on the news, she checked the number cautiously before opening it and discovered a charming photo of a familiar black Labrador with a one-line caption: *Please don't forget us. R.*

She passed the phone across to her mother who glanced at it and smiled indulgently. 'That's rather nice, isn't it?'

'He's a very nice dog.'

'That's not what I meant.'

'I know what you meant. I must admit it would be good to talk to Rob. With his background, I'm sure he'd be able to understand the sort of stress I've been through today.'

'Well, why don't you call him?' Her mum grinned and stood up. 'It's all right. I'm going into the kitchen to make two mugs of hot chocolate. I promise I won't listen. Go ahead and call him.'

After a few seconds of reflection, Steph pressed the video call button and waited. Rob must have been holding the phone as he answered almost immediately, and his face appeared on the screen. 'Steph, hi. It's great to hear from you. I've been following the various news stories. Royalty and you are big news all over the world. There was even a piece on the TV here in Italy. How's it going?'

In spite of her doubts, seeing him and hearing his voice sent a thrill of pleasure through her that she couldn't stop. She found herself smiling back at him as she answered. 'It's been exhausting… and far more intrusive than I was expecting.'

'When you say intrusive, might that be a reference to the photos of you on the beach that are doing the rounds?'

'I swear with every new photo I see, the bikini gets smaller and smaller. Are they allowed to play around with images like that? It makes me feel like a page three model.'

'You look a damn sight better than any page three model.' There was a momentary hesitation before he corrected himself. 'Sorry, I promised myself I wouldn't start throwing out compliments.'

She couldn't help herself. 'And why's that?'

'You really want to know?'

'Of course.'

She had to wait a few seconds while he formulated his reply. 'Because I didn't want you to think I was still behaving like the old me.'

'You're telling me you're no longer the old you?'

'I'd like to think so.'

'So would I.' She came close to asking him why, in that case, he had been kissing the fingers of some woman – his accompanist or another random woman – in Sanremo, but she stifled the impulse. To do so would risk turning this conversation into what her mother had described as a scene, and the telephone was the wrong medium for one of those. Instead, she decided to get back onto safer ground.

'Where are you now? Didn't you say you were off to Eastern Europe?'

'I'm due in Prague in two days' time but I'm in Milan at the moment, desperately looking for a new accompanist.'

Steph's ears pricked up. 'Why, what happened to the old one? What was her name…?'

'Anna Maria – she's gone to live in Boston with her partner. I'm afraid I've lost her.'

'Had you been together long?' As an accompanist or more? Mind you, reference to a 'partner' was interesting…

'Three years. It's been a long time. She knew my work so well, and we were very close.'

Steph couldn't restrain a little prod. 'When you say, "very close", how close?'

To her surprise, he laughed. 'As close as I could be to somebody whose partner's called Virginia.'

The penny dropped. 'Ah, I see.' If he was telling the truth about his accompanist's sexuality, this let him off the hook – assuming she had been the woman Willow claimed to have seen. 'And she's already left for the States?'

'A couple of weeks ago now. We had our last meal together in Sanremo after the concert, and she and Virginia flew out two days later.'

Steph's mind was racing. It would appear that he was innocent of any wrongdoing – at least as far as Sanremo was concerned – and this meant she was guilty of misjudging him. She felt simultaneously ashamed and excited. Might this mean…? To give herself time to think, she asked him how he was doing in his search for a replacement accompanist, and he asked her how the recording was going. They chatted for several minutes before he came up with a suggestion.

'My concert in Prague's on Thursday night. I was wondering about coming over to London after it in the hope that you and I could meet up.'

'Bugger!' Steph was quick to explain her outburst. 'Sorry, Rob, but we're all flying across to LA on Thursday. There's a big showbiz party on Friday night and then we're supposedly going to be staying in America for weeks and weeks.'

'Bugger, indeed.' There was a pause while he rethought things. 'Are you likely to be back for the third of November?'

'As far as I know, I think so. Sol and Zach are talking about us being in the States for all of October so we should be back at the end of the month, but I can check. Why do you ask?'

'I'm playing at the Royal Albert Hall on November the third and I could stay on in London for a few days if you're going to be about. I'd really like to see you.'

'And I'd really like to see you, too.' Steph knew she had no hesitation. 'And if I can get tickets to the concert, I'd love to come. I'll check with Sol as soon as we get to LA and let you know whether I'll be back in time.'

'I can send you tickets to the concert. I'd be delighted if you were there. What address should I use?'

'Send them to Mum's house. I'll stay with her when I'm back in London.'

She dictated the address to him and then they chatted a bit more, but by the time he rang off she was feeling seriously disappointed that she wouldn't see him for a full month. Once again she found herself confronted with the problems created by her new job. Although the media interest was causing her grief, she was very keen to make a go of it and help make the new version of Royalty as famous as the old one. On the other hand, every day she spent with the band was another day away from Rob and the more she thought of him, the more she wished there was some way they could be together.

But there wasn't.

Chapter 23

They flew first class to California and to Steph it all felt surreal. Here she was, the same person who little more than a month earlier had been saving up to take her mum to see a Shakespeare play in Stratford-upon-Avon, and yet now money was no object, and she was being fêted like real royalty. Keith and the others looked much more relaxed, but of course they had much more experience of this sort of luxury than she did. Faye and the other two wives flew out with them for Friday's gala party but wouldn't be accompanying them on what sounded like an exhausting tour of the continent over the course of the next four weeks. During this time the band would be meeting members of the press and TV, doing countless interviews, and shooting the videos to accompany the new album. The first of these was to be shot somewhere in the heart of the Colorado Desert and the other in the Everglades of Florida. Although Steph was looking forward to seeing the sights, the prospect of being bitten by a rattlesnake or an alligator was nothing compared to the thought that Sol's 'people' might try to get her to strip to her bikini again.

They were greeted at LAX by a noisy crowd of fans and although Steph had managed to grab a few hours' sleep on the plane, she was feeling tired and confused as they were escorted through immigration and out into the warm California air. The clock in the Arrival area told her it was seven o'clock in the evening, but her body was telling her it was the middle of the night. They were ferried in a limo to the legendary Beverly Hills Hotel on Sunset Boulevard, where she almost bumped into none other than Tom Cruise as she walked in. Her eyes opened wide in amazement and stayed that way as she was led to a suite twice the size of Ethan's flat, and this was for her sole use. By this time the lack of sleep was catching up with her, so she refused the offer of food and decided to crash out.

Although she woke a few times during the night, she slept remarkably well and was wide awake at eight o'clock when the phone in the room started ringing. It was Keith, telling her to order breakfast in her room and to be ready for a meeting with Sol and the team at ten. He was sounding remarkably perky for an almost sixty-year-old.

The limo was waiting out front at nine thirty and Steph found that Keith was already inside, checking his watch fretfully. 'Hi, Steph, sleep well?'

'Better than I thought…'

He didn't give her a chance to elaborate as his eyes were still on his watch, his fingers drumming restlessly on his knee. 'Ben and Johnny were never good at timekeeping. I'm giving them another two minutes and then I'm going in to haul them out.' He sounded genuinely irked.

Fortunately, a minute later the other two arrived. A uniformed porter closed the door silently and Zach pressed a few dollar bills into his hand before taking a seat up front alongside the driver. The glass screen separating them slid quietly down and Zach swivelled round and explained the plan for the day.

'Business meeting this morning for everybody, party in the evening. Meet in the lobby at seven thirty. Steph, you have an appointment with Bexley at two. Okay?'

'Who's Bexley?' Steph wasn't sure what this might herald.

Zach's answer was puzzling. 'She's your style guru.'

'Style guru? What's that?' Although she had a horrible feeling she knew, and it soon turned out that she was right.

'She'll take you shopping. You need to look your best tonight for the party, and you need a choice of outfits to take with us on the road.' In response to the expression on her face he caught her eye and explained. 'Like it or not, you're a young woman, and young women in our world are expected to look good.'

'Oh, God…' She could have said a whole lot more, and worse, but she bit her tongue, limiting herself to, 'I have no intention of being turned into some sort of bimbo, Zach.'

'No, not at all. You're great as you are. Just a bit of bling for the cameras.'

The 'bit of bling for the cameras' turned out to be a major undertaking. Bexley was a very smart woman who was probably in her early forties but could easily have passed for Steph's age. She greeted Steph warmly and led her out to a waiting car. The first stop was a salon where Steph's long hair was washed, trimmed and curled up on her head in a striking style that she had to admit did look pretty good. Bexley suggested Steph should consider a more radical 'new look', which would involve shaving most of the right side of her head, but Steph dug her heels in and refused the offer. She also said no to false eyelashes the size of scary spiders, false nails the length of eagle talons and resolutely shook her head at the idea of lip filler. Disappointed but undeterred, Bexley then bundled her back into the car and took her to a series of hideously expensive boutiques where they very quickly clocked up thousands of dollars' worth of clothes that Bexley paid for with a gold card. Among these purchases was the dress for tonight's party.

As Steph changed in and out of different outfits, ending up with tonight's blue silk gown, Bexley explained what awaited the band at this evening's party. 'The company's rented the Crystal Ballroom at your hotel and we're expecting around two hundred guests.' She gave Steph a little smile. 'I guarantee you'll recognise at least half of them, even if you've never met them in your life. When Sol throws a party like this, all the stars come out of the woodwork.' She cast a long, critical glance at Steph's gown. 'I would have preferred a bit more skin on show, but this one does look good on you all the same.'

Steph shook her head as she studied herself in the mirror. 'I'm not a skin-on-show sort of girl, Bexley. As for this dress, although it doesn't have a plunging neckline, it's so lightweight and sheer, I feel half naked.'

Bexley nodded sagely. 'That's a thought. We need to get you some new underwear. Slip the dress off and give it to the salesperson. She'll pack it up for you while we head for the lingerie department.'

When Bexley dropped Steph off at the hotel just before six, it needed a porter with a trolley to cart all the bags up to her suite. She realised as she started unpacking everything that she was going to have to buy another suitcase, probably two, just to hold all the new stuff. She took a long, relaxing bath – taking care not to get her hair wet – and then slipped into her new underwear and the gown. When she checked herself in the mirror she had to admit that Bexley had got it dead right. The blue of the silk was almost exactly the same shade as the blue of her eyes. Finally, she fixed on the new earrings and stepped into the new heels that made her about three inches taller. She checked her watch and saw that it was almost time to meet the others in the lobby, so she drained a glass of ice water and headed out to face the music – literally.

The moment she stepped out of the lift in the lobby all hell broke loose as flashlights nearly blinded her. There was a scrum of reporters and photographers waiting for her, but standing in front of them, fortunately, were Zach and Vic who positioned themselves on either side of her and steered her through the crowd to the ballroom. A wave of the hand from Zach to the trio of hefty bouncers allowed her through with her guardians, but left the media scrum outside, still desperately trying to attract her attention. In here the first person she saw was Keith, looking unusually smart in a tuxedo. Beside him was Faye, looking gorgeous in grey silk. Her eyes lit up as she saw Steph.

'Wow, Steph, you certainly scrub up well. You look amazing.'

'Not as amazing as you do. I love that dress. As for me, I feel like I'm on display.'

'That's exactly what you are.' Keith gave her a broad smile. 'Our newest and most attractive band member. I'm afraid everybody's going to be looking at you.'

'Oh God…'

'You'll get used to it.' He took her arm. 'Now come and let me introduce you to some people. Have you met Paul McCartney?'

The next hour was a dizzying series of encounters with household names from the music business, the cinema and even the world of American politics. At last she managed to extract herself from a group including one former president, a baseball legend whose name meant nothing to her, and a Goth girl who was currently number one in the charts. She was hiding in a corner behind a huge flower arrangement, sipping ice water, and wishing she was somewhere else, anywhere else, when she heard a familiar voice.

'Ah, that's where you are. I've been looking everywhere for you.'

Such was her amazement, she almost spilt her water all over her new gown. 'Rob! What on earth are you doing here?'

'I had to see you and, boy, do you look good!'

She set down her glass on a nearby table and took a close look at him as her emotions bubbled to the surface. He looked very smart and most appealing in his tuxedo, and she didn't hesitate to reach out to catch hold of him and pull him close enough so she could kiss him on the lips. Wearing her new heels, she hardly needed to stretch up to do so. She felt his arms wrap themselves around her as he kissed her in return. It was just as well he was holding her tightly as she might have collapsed on the floor. The kiss simply took her breath away and it was with real regret that she finally took a tentative step back, still holding his hands in both of hers.

'Wow!' She smiled at him and blinked a few times. 'Wow... that was worth the wait.'

He was smiling as well. 'You can say that again. You want to know something? I've wanted to do that since the very first moment I laid eyes on you on the beach that time.'

'That time you barely uttered a couple of syllables or the next time when I only got three words out of you? I was convinced you didn't like me.'

'The very opposite. It was as if a hammer had hit me on the back of the head when I saw you, and I suddenly realised what I'd been missing all these years. I'm sorry I was so uncommunicative at first, but I was terrified I'd scare you off.'

She grinned at him. 'You sound like Johnny talking about his beloved fly fishing.' She stopped a passing waiter and grabbed two glasses of champagne. 'I don't know about you, but I could do with a proper drink.'

–

The sunlight shining in through the blinds woke her early and she opened her eyes and blinked. A movement beside her made her turn her head and she saw him propped up on one elbow, staring down at her.

'*Buongiorno, signora.*'

'*Buongiorno, signore.* It's good to see you.'

'Not as good as it is to see you. I've been watching you sleep for maybe an hour now.' He reached down and brushed a lock of hair from her face. 'As shows go, it was one of the best. I could have spent all day just looking at you.'

She rubbed her cheek against him and stared up at him. 'You don't look too bad yourself.' She kissed the side of his chest and then looked up again. 'So, what's the plan? How long have I got you for?'

'I think the question should be, how long have I got *you* for? Dad told me last night that you guys are off to San Francisco tomorrow, then Seattle, Vancouver, and any number of places in Canada before coming back to the States again en route to Mexico.'

She shook her head ruefully. 'And didn't you say you've got a tour in Germany coming up?'

'Starting on Tuesday.'

'As soon as that? And you flew all the way from Europe just for a couple of days? I've been meaning to ask: did you manage to get yourself fixed up with a new accompanist?'

'I'd have flown all the way just for the sake of a couple of *hours* with you. As for my new accompanist, the answer's yes and no. Yes, for the next few weeks – an old friend doing me a favour – but I'm going to have to start looking properly before the end of the month.' His eyes twinkled. 'I don't suppose I can lure you away from Royalty? I'm afraid the money's not so good.'

'I know which I'd rather do, but I've promised your dad and the others now, so I'm stuck.' She corrected herself. 'Sorry, that sounds so ungrateful, but you know what I mean.'

'I know; I was just kidding. Of course you're committed. By the way, I'm a bit concerned about Dad. It sounds as though he's getting as obsessive about the band as he used to be. I hope he doesn't scare the other two off.'

'Johnny and Ben said the same thing. Hopefully they'll have it out with him. I'm the new girl, so I feel it's not up to me. So, what this means as far as you and I are concerned is that I've got you for today, and then that's about that.'

As she spoke the room phone started ringing and she stretched over his body to answer it. His skin felt really good against hers and she was almost purring as she picked up the phone.

'Morning, Steph, Sol's team have booked us an interview at CBS at eleven. The car will pick us up at ten thirty. Don't be late, okay?' It was Keith and he barely gave her time to reply before hanging up, presumably so as to be able to bully the other band members into getting up as well. She dropped the phone but stayed where she was, now looking down into Rob's eyes from above.

'We don't have a lot of time.'

As she bent down to kiss him, she heard him murmur. 'Mustn't waste it then…'

Chapter 24

The rest of the month was a blur of different cities but remarkably similar hotels, limos, private planes, interviews and studios. Steph worked her way through – and even augmented – her stock of new clothes, gradually got used to having cameras pointed at her, and refined her answers to stock questions like, 'How does it feel to be the first woman in Royalty?' She enjoyed seeing places she had only heard about until now, but found that she had very little free time for sightseeing, and on the rare occasions when she could get out, an increasing number of people were starting to recognise her face and stop her for photos or autographs. Although such fame had been her dream since her teenage years, it made her feel very self-conscious.

All the time Rob wasn't far from her thoughts. They called each other most days, but with the time difference this meant that the moments she really would have liked to hear the sound of his voice – like when she was getting ready for bed – she knew that he was probably sitting down to breakfast. It made their relationship feel ever more insubstantial. She had cried when he'd left her to fly back to Europe and even now, weeks later, the thought of him could produce a poignant mix of smiles and tears. There was no longer any doubt in her mind that he was

The One, and she relayed this information to her mum who asked the inevitable question.

'What are you going to do about it? Presumably you'll be back over here in a few weeks. Are you planning on getting together with him? Maybe go and stay with him and his lovely dog?'

'You can't imagine how much I'd love to, Mum, but it's not as easy as that. We've got our first concert coming up at the beginning of December, and Keith says we'll need to spend a lot of November in the studio in London practising for it. He's even talking about what he calls an "impromptu" concert here in the States before we leave, and we're going to be in a studio in Detroit for a few days this week, to get ready for it. I barely have time to eat and sleep.'

'So what you're saying is that your job's going to keep you and Rob apart?'

'That's exactly what I'm saying, at least for quite a few months or even a year, as we go on tour, promoting the reformed band and the new album.'

'Well, surely if he feels the same way about you as you do about him, he'll wait until you're freer. He does feel the same way about you, doesn't he?'

'I think so… in fact I'm pretty sure he does, but the truth is that we've spent so little time together. Maybe if we remain apart for too long he'll change his mind. Don't forget his track record with women.'

'Rubbish. You've told me yourself you think he's a changed man. He'll wait for you, I know it.'

'But how long for?'

'I suppose the alternative is that you tell Keith and the others that you've changed your mind and you want to leave the band.'

'Don't think I haven't considered it. The thing is though that I just can't do something like that to them. Apart from the fact that I've signed a contract, I owe it to them to stick with it although I'd be lying if I said I enjoyed all the baggage that comes with fame. If it was just the music, I'd be fine, but I feel like my life's no longer my own.'

'Just remember that your health and happiness are the most important things.'

'You're right. The guys tell me the media attention will calm down with time and I should still be happy, even if it has to be without Rob.' Her mum made no response but both of them could hear the doubt in her voice.

Making the new videos provided a couple of days of diversion. To the director's chagrin, Steph dug her heels in and refused to appear in a bikini – particularly one of a selection of microscopic bikinis Bexley had insisted on buying for her in LA – but she had to agree to appearing in the sort of revealing tops and short skirts she would never normally have dreamt of wearing. Ben and Johnny provided reassurance and support for her, although Keith was getting ever more domineering as far as what she and the others should do. Ben reported to her one night that he and Johnny had taken him to one side earlier in the day and tried to convince him to chill out but had had little success. Ben even muttered darkly, 'If he carries on like this, I might chuck the whole thing in, just like I was thinking of doing before Vince's death.'

This left Steph with mixed feelings. If Ben really did pull out of the band, maybe even accompanied by Johnny, that would surely signal the death knell of Royalty and, with it, the sudden end to her very short career as a rock star. Although her eye-watering salary and the share of royalties on the new album would keep her going for ages, it would be frustrating to see her big break dissolve into thin air. On the other hand – and far more important in her eyes – was the fact that the demise of Royalty would allow her to spend much more time with Rob. As long as he still wanted her.

The impromptu concert took place right at the end of October when they were back in California once more. Sol's company had rented Santa Monica Pier for the event and by the time Steph and the band arrived there at sundown there were thousands of people crowding the beach. Despite being a free concert, Keith had asked for donations towards his World Hunger Trust, and volunteers with collecting buckets squeezed in and out of the throng of people. As well as the lucky onlookers who managed to find a place on the sand, the concert was also being filmed and broadcast live across the world, and a hastily erected grandstand was packed with journalists and music critics who would further spread the word of the group's resurrection to anyone who hadn't yet heard.

As Steph stood at the side of the stage, apprehensively waiting to go on, she felt a touch on her arm. It was Faye, who had flown in specially for the occasion.

'Feeling nervous?'

'Terrified.' They hugged. 'It's great to see you, Faye.'

'And you. Don't be frightened. It'll go wonderfully, I'm sure. I'm glad I got to you before you went on. I have a message for you from Rob. He says he's missing you terribly and he can't wait to see you again.' Faye's eyes sparkled. 'I can't tell you how happy I am that you've found each other.'

'Not as happy as I am. The trouble is that he's got his life and now I've got this life and it looks like never the twain shall meet.'

'You'll sort yourselves out, don't you worry.'

At that moment the lights of the stage were extinguished, and an expectant hush spread throughout the audience. Keith materialised at Steph's side with the other two. 'It's show time, folks! Come on, let's show them Royalty are back, even better than ever!'

Steph barely felt Faye kiss her on the cheek before Keith led them out onto the stage. There was just enough light for her to see her way, trying desperately not to trip over anything as she crept around all the paraphernalia to her keyboards. The audience must have spotted movement as a groundswell of noise started to rise up in a low rumble. Seconds later the lightshow started with flashing lasers and strobes, while the video of them in the Everglades appeared on the huge screen behind them. The noise from the crowd became a roar and she only just heard Johnny beat time with one drumstick against the other as he called out, 'One, two, three, four.' And they were off.

Although she subsequently learnt that the show had lasted over two hours, it felt as though it was over in a matter of minutes. The presence of the crowd, like an invisible animal out there roaring and screaming, was unnerving at first, but she gradually got used to it and when she produced just about her best ever performance of the piano solo from the group's former hit, 'Getting Back on Top', she could distinctly hear the crowd chanting 'Steph, Steph, Steph' and it felt good.

The final number was 'Never Too Late', Ben's homage to Vince, and it reduced the thousands out there on the beach to near silence. As Steph looked out over the crowd, all she could see was a mass of moving lights as people held up their phones and swayed in time to the music. The audience then erupted into a massive outpouring of delighted applause as the last notes of the guitar echoed around the pier. The stage lights came on, effectively blinding her to the crowd on the beach and she looked across at the other members of the band. Keith was beaming, Johnny wiping his face with a towel, and Ben quite obviously in tears. Relinquishing her place at the keyboards, Steph made her way across to him and enveloped him in a hug.

'Wonderful, Ben, just wonderful. Vince would have been so pleased, I'm sure.'

He gave her a grateful smile and wiped his eyes, clearly too emotional to speak. The noise from the audience rose even higher until it changed into a chant, demanding more. Giving Ben a quick kiss on the cheek, she hurried back to her piano as Keith turned towards them and indicated they would play one more number. This was 'Summer Nights', one of the old ones, and it started with one of his best-known guitar solos. Steph looked on in fascination as the guitar riff split the night air. Keith raised the guitar to the heavens, a single spotlight on him, and played like a man possessed, not missing a single note. When he came to the end of his solo the audience erupted once more and Steph and the others joined in with their instruments and the song continued at full volume for ten minutes.

She looked across at Johnny over the top of her keyboard as she played and saw him give her a huge grin. That's when she realised that she had been grin-ning wildly at him. All her pre-show nerves had faded away and she'd genuinely enjoyed herself, savouring the atmosphere, knowing that she had just fulfilled a dream. The light show behind them rose in intensity as the number they were playing approached its climax, and when it finally ended, the sky above them exploded into a blinding and deafening firework display. To equally deafening applause from the audience on the beach, they filed off stage and Steph joined the others in waving back at the fans and the TV cameras, filled with an overwhelming sensation of achievement. She had done it. She was now a fully fledged member of one of the greatest bands that had ever existed. Overcome by a sudden wave of exhaustion, she stumbled offstage into the wings, slumped down on a packing case and burst into tears.

She sat there and her thoughts returned once more to her father. She now knew what he must have felt when he had been in iconic concert halls, performing with the orchestra, and for a moment she felt his very real presence alongside her. She dropped her head into her hands and sobbed, unsure whether out of grief or joy.

Seconds later she felt somebody sit down beside her and a comforting arm stretch around her shoulders. It was Ben. 'Let it out, Steph, it's all right to cry. It's the most natural thing in the world. You were great, just great. I'm so happy for you, for all of us.'

Steph buried her head in his chest for over a minute before she felt the tears slow and then stop. She straightened up, wiping her hands across her eyes, and kissed him on the cheek.

'Thanks, Ben, I'm sorry about that, I don't know what just happened.'

'It's the adrenalin. It's been pumping through your body for a couple of hours and now, suddenly, the tap's been turned off. It happens to all of us.' He pointed across to where Keith was hugging Faye. 'Even our lord and master himself.' He raised his voice and bellowed over to the others. 'Royalty's back, guys! You'd better believe it!'

One of the roadies appeared with towels and Steph took one gratefully, burying her face in it, realising for the first time that she was soaked in sweat. Seconds later she felt a cold bottle of water being pressed into her hand and she tore off the top and upended it into her mouth and over her face before mopping herself down with the towel one more.

A familiar voice roused her. 'That was fantastic, Steph. Now let's get you changed. The media are waiting to talk to you all, and you need to look good.'

Steph emerged from the towel to see that it was her style guru, Bexley. 'Hi, Bex. Did you say we've got to do an interview right now?'

Bexley nodded and glanced at her watch. 'You and I have exactly fourteen minutes to get you out of those clothes, into the shower and into fresh clothes. You coming?'

Thirteen and a half minutes later Steph was rushed out of her changing room and joined the three men under the lights of the TV crew. The interviewer was a well-known face and mercifully he and Keith between them did most of the talking while she did her best to relax and drained yet another bottle of water. By the time the questions came around to her she had at least had time to catch her breath and collect herself a bit.

'Hey, Steph, that was great. How did it feel out there on stage?' The TV host, brimming with bonhomie, transferred his attention to her and she saw a now familiar microphone on its boom swing towards her. She took a deep breath and replied.

'I'm still trying to come to terms with it myself. Being out there alongside legends like Keith, Ben and Johnny has been my dream – has probably been the dream of thousands, maybe millions of people – for so long that I still can hardly believe it's happened. Tell me this isn't a dream, would you?'

'This is no dream, Steph, and you and the rest of the band were terrific.'

He then produced a volley of questions, which she managed to deal with pretty well after a month of practice, before he finally offered her the chance to pass on her own message. 'Steph, this is being broadcast all over the world so do you have anything you'd like to say to anybody? Your family maybe or somebody special?' The innuendo in his voice was as obvious as the cheeky grin on his face.

'If my mum's watching, I'd like to tell her I love her – although I'm sure she knows that. And I'd like to thank her for all her love and support… along with my dad, of course.' Her voice faltered for a moment. 'If it hadn't been for his influence none of this would have happened.' While she reached for a tissue and wiped her eyes an idea came to her. 'And as for a message to somebody special, I'd like to send lots of love to Waldorf, my perfect companion.'

'Waldorf, that's some name!'

'He's some guy.' This time she wasn't talking about the Labrador.

Chapter 25

All the way back across to the UK she couldn't stop her brain from churning. Once the euphoria of the concert had begun to subside, she had found herself reflecting ever harder on this new life of hers and on the position in which she now found herself. The concert had been terrifying, gruelling, but immensely satisfying, and she could still feel a terrific buzz inside even now after three days. It had been an uplifting experience and she knew she would never forget it. The media had reacted in an overwhelmingly positive way to the concert, and photos of the band – and her face in particular – were now popping up all over the place on magazine covers and newspaper hoardings, catapulting her from obscurity into the limelight. She had become an overnight sensation and she still didn't know if she was going to be able to cope with the pressures this produced on her and her private life – or at least, what little was left of her privacy. It really had been a baptism of fire, but she was looking forward to their next concert, scheduled to take place at the O2 Arena in London in just over a month's time.

On a personal level, this only increased her problems. There was no doubt in her mind that she had enjoyed performing on stage and she wanted to do more of it. Yes, the media attention was a pain, but there was no getting away from the fact that she could see herself staying with

Royalty for years to come. The three men had rapidly become a second family to her, and she owed it to them to do her best for the group and for herself. The downside to this was the inevitability that this would take her ever further from Rob and deep down inside she was already admitting to herself, even if not to anybody else, that she loved him. The binary choice was ever starker – Royalty or Rob.

The recurring thought running around and around in her head was whether maybe the band had now become the real love of her life. She knew she wanted to keep her place in the band, but she also wanted Rob. The sad reality of the situation was that – at least for now – she was going to have to choose between the two. In fact, she reminded herself as the aircraft landed at Heathrow, the choice was already made. As she had told her mother, she had signed a contract that bound her to Royalty for the foreseeable future and in return guaranteed her financial security for life. Yes, she should be able to see Rob, maybe even snatch a few weekends with him and Waldorf in Italy, but Sol and Keith had both warned her in no uncertain terms that her life for the next few years was likely to be busy and nomadic as Royalty toured the globe. Add to that the fact that Rob's own career took him off all over the world, and the chances of them being able to spend quality time together appeared slim. She couldn't help wondering if Rob was having similar thoughts, trying to also decide between his travel-heavy career and their nascent relationship...

Apart from the next Royalty concert in December, there was another concert not far from her thoughts and this was scheduled to take place in just two days. This one was to be at the Royal Albert Hall in London and the star of the show was to be Rob Sinclair, aka the love of her life.

Or was he?

After landing in London, they were escorted through a crowd of fans and transferred to a lesser-known luxury hotel on the fringes of Chelsea, where Keith told her they should be able to keep a low profile while they took part in interviews and chat shows on different TV channels as well as rehearsing for the O2 concert. As before, Steph protested that she preferred to stay with her mum, but the others advised her to hold on to her hotel room in case the media got wind of her return to her roots. She very quickly discovered that they were right, when she headed off to see her mum. As her cab drove along the street towards the house, she spotted half a dozen people hanging about on the pavement at the front, most carrying cameras. She crouched down on the seat and told the driver not to stop. Instead, she got him to drop her around the corner, and she sneaked back along the narrow alley at the rear of the row of houses. Letting herself into the garden by the back gate she hurried across the lawn and tapped on the French windows. Seconds later she was inside, hugging her mum.

With the net curtains closed, they were able to sit down on the sofa and catch up unobserved. Her mother had been following the progress of the group across North America and had even recorded the coverage of the Santa Monica concert. She offered to play it to Steph who shook her head.

'I know it by heart, Mum. It was an experience I'll never forget.'

'You were so good; the whole group was. Tell me; did your Rob come over to see you play?'

'No, he was in Stockholm for a concert of his own that night, but we spoke on the phone.'

'And how are things between the two of you?'

'Things are great… when we're together. The trouble is that that's not very often. I haven't seen him for a month.'

'Well, we're going to see him the day after tomorrow.'

'We?'

Her mum nodded triumphantly and reached for an envelope on the coffee table. It was addressed to *Gentilissima Signora Zanin* and inside were two tickets and backstage passes to Rob's concert at the Royal Albert Hall.

'There's a lovely note along with the tickets, inviting me to come to the concert and then to come for dinner afterwards.' She gave Steph a beaming smile. 'Isn't that sweet of him?'

'It really is. I hope you like him when you meet him.'

'I have no doubt about that at all.'

'I hope so. At least I can guarantee you'll enjoy the concert.'

When they got to the concert on Friday night, it was to find that their seats were in one of the very best boxes, looking down onto the stage from close range. The auditorium was full and there was an expectant hush in the huge concert hall. Steph and her mum soon discovered that they would be sharing the box with one other person. This was a grey-haired lady in her sixties or early seventies who introduced herself to them as Dulcie Dooley and Steph immediately recognised the name.

'How lovely to meet you. Rob's told me all about you.' She turned to her mum. 'Mrs Dooley was Rob's music teacher, the person who first set him on course to becoming a violinist.' She glanced back at Mrs Dooley.

'And, from what he told me, you were his surrogate mum when he was all alone at boarding school.'

'I had a very soft spot for Robert. I still have. It's lovely to meet you, too, Stephanie. Robert called me the other day and told me who you are, but I would have recognised your face anyway from the TV. How exciting for me to meet such a famous and successful musician.'

'Any fame is very recent, Mrs Dooley. I'm still getting used to seeing my face in the papers.'

'And I gather Robert's taking us all out for dinner tonight. How wonderful!'

It was indeed a wonderful evening. The concert, with a full orchestra, was all Mozart and started with his Violin Concerto No. 3. As the conductor led the orchestra into the introduction, Steph was able to concentrate her attention on the soloist. He was dressed in an immaculate dark suit, and he was looking serious as he stood in front of the crowd, violin and bow at the ready, waiting for his cue to begin. She couldn't help remembering the nervous tension she had felt before the concert in Santa Monica and she wondered whether he was even a fraction as tense as she had been, despite all his experience. Then, for a split second, she felt sure she saw him glance upwards towards the box and there might even have been a hint of a smile on his face. This tiny smile – more imagined than observed – sent a warm glow throughout her whole body that lasted the entire concert. Suddenly she found herself questioning her resolve to stick with Royalty. Maybe her mum was right, and her personal happiness depended more on this man than on any stage performance.

The concert was a great success and finished just after ten. Steph waited with her mum and Mrs Dooley until the crowds had subsided before heading backstage with their special VIP passes. They found Rob already showered and changed and ready to go. Steph waited until he had greeted Mrs Dooley with kisses to her cheeks and her mother had greeted him with kisses to his cheeks, before she held out her arms to him.

'*Ciao, bello*. I've missed you.'

He caught hold of her hands and pulled her towards him. '*Ciao, bella*. I've missed you too.' And he kissed her. In view of the present company, it wasn't a long or passionate kiss, but it reached deep inside her all the same.

They took a cab from the concert hall and Steph was surprised to find that he had booked a table at the Ritz. Mrs Dooley and Steph's mum stepped out and gazed in awe at this world-famous establishment while Rob stayed back so he could take Steph's hand and whisper in her ear.

'I thought they might enjoy a little treat. Of course, now you're a global megastar, places like this must be old hat to you.'

'Don't you believe it. The Ritz is still the Ritz. It feels unbelievable that I'm here in a place like this.' She glanced across to where the two ladies were conversing and lowered her voice. 'Although room service with you in my hotel room would have been preferable.'

He leant in and kissed her again. 'How about breakfast in bed?'

'Sounds perfect.'

Dinner was predictably excellent. They opted not to go for either the five-course or the seven-course Epicurean menus and Steph and Rob opted for halibut with fennel and lemon while her mum and Mrs Dooley chose duck with beetroot and lavender. For dessert they all decided in favour of Seville orange soufflé with Grand Marnier and vanilla, and everything tasted as good as they had been expecting.

The only disappointment was the discovery that Rob would be off very soon on a tour of Japan and the Far East for three whole weeks until the end of November and he would only be back a few days before the big O2 concert. This meant that Steph only had him for tonight and tomorrow and then he was due back in Italy for a performance in Rome before flying east. Almost another month would pass before she could be with him again. It was exasperating.

When she woke up next morning and looked at him sleeping peacefully at her side, her exasperation grew. Was this all they could accept: a few hours snatched together every now and then? How could a relationship survive if they kept missing each other like ships passing in the night? Was it all destined for disaster?

'You're looking very serious.' His voice interrupted her thoughts and she ducked down to kiss him softly on the lips.

'I'm *feeling* very serious. Do you realise we've only got today and then you're off to Italy, I'm off to some TV studio, and then you're going away to the Far East? The next time I see you is going to be in a month.'

His expression became equally serious. 'You don't need to remind me. If there was any way to change things I would, but as you can imagine, the Far East tour was arranged almost a year ago and there are thousands of tickets sold. There's no way I can duck out of it now.'

She snuggled up against him and felt his arm encircle her shoulders. 'I'm in the same boat. As far as I can see, every single day this month and next is already earmarked for something. Between them, your dad and the record company have got Royalty working flat out. Then we're off on our own Far East tour in January. There's no way I can wriggle out of any of it.' She rubbed her cheek against the side of his chest. 'Star-crossed lovers, that's what we are. Shakespeare knew a thing or two, didn't he?'

'He certainly did, but the irony here is that, unlike Romeo and Juliet, things for us are the way they are because that's what we've chosen, not because some malignant external force is imposing them on us.' She felt his hand run up her arm to her shoulder and begin to caress her hair. In spite of the seriousness of their conversation she nuzzled even closer against him and purred as he continued. 'We both love our jobs and that's that. I could no more ask you to give up your new career in Royalty than you could expect me to put down my violin and take up olive growing.' She felt his lips against her forehead. 'Not that the idea hasn't crossed my mind a few times – you know, outside in the open air with Waldorf to keep me company, the sun shining, the sound of the waves in the background, you at my side. You have to admit it does have its attraction.'

'And I could help you pick the olives and grapes, and we could make our own wine and olive oil.' She sighed wistfully. 'But it'll never happen; at least not for a long time.'

He leant down and kissed her with real passion before pulling back, his eyes staring into hers. 'All joking apart, over the past weeks, I've seriously considered giving up the violin for you, you know. I'd miss it, but I'd have something far more important. The more I get to know you, the more I realise that you're the most important thing in the world; more important than my music, more important than my family, more important even than my

Chapter 26

The rest of November was hectic. Steph had been right in thinking that every day would be taken up with a combination of PR appearances, interviews and considerable time spent in the East London studio honing and refining the group's performance in readiness for the O2 event at the beginning of December. She found herself in demand from all sides and appeared almost on a daily basis on programmes as diverse as *Blue Peter* and *Newsnight* and in publications as varied as *Time* magazine and *Vogue*.

It didn't take long for the glamour to wane. Yes, it was exciting to find that she had become a celebrity, but all too soon she realised that she wasn't cut from celebrity cloth. She had always valued her privacy and now, in one sweep, she had become public property, and it was growing ever more uncomfortable. Rather than gradually getting used to and accepting these constant intrusions into her personal life, as the weeks went by she found them harder and harder to bear.

She had followed Keith and Ben's advice and had deleted her social media presence, but not before she had started to receive some disturbing, disgusting and downright scary messages from all over the globe. She was now resigned to the appearance of paparazzi at the most inconvenient moments, and even simple things like visiting her mum rapidly assumed the appearance of covert operations. This was, as Keith continued to remind her, a natural consequence of her newfound fame, but she soon began to feel more like a hunted animal.

The complication was that she loved performing. The buzz she had got from her very first concert had been incomparable, and she knew she would be devastated to give that up, but the fact of the matter was that it was only too clear that the thrill of live performance came with undesirable side-effects, and she wasn't going to be able to have one without the other.

Gradually as the days went by, she began seriously considering plan B – what to do if she really did give up life with the band. The problem was that, for now at least, there was no plan B, and she spent hours in lonely hotel rooms turning over alternative ideas. Like it or not, she was now a celebrity. Was there any way she could capitalise on her fame to create a new career for herself which would remove her from the limelight? Using her celebrity to achieve anonymity seemed like an oxymoron but surely there had to be some way...

She spoke to Rob almost every day, although as soon as he flew off to Japan the same old problem of the time difference between them raised its head and communication became ever more fraught. She wished with all her heart that there could be some way of spending more time together but she owed it to the band to stick with them.

For his part, Rob told her he had been missing her hugely and he gave her a shock one evening in a video call from Tokyo. He was sitting on the end of his bed wearing what looked like a kimono and, behind him, she could see the remains of a breakfast tray on a table beyond which was the ultra-modern skyline of the city.

In the meantime, Faye and Lottie, in particular, had taken her under their wing and taught her the best ways of managing to avoid the media and continue to lead a vaguely normal life. In the studio Steph was able to relax and she enjoyed playing with the band more and more. In the course of the practice sessions Keith spotted that she had a good voice and she found herself promoted to lead singer for some of the numbers. On several occasions she came close to telling him of her decision to cut right back on her extra-curricular commitments, but she stuck to her plan of breaking it to the band after the O2 concert.

As the big day approached, Steph began to feel that same mix of apprehension and anticipation she had experienced before going on stage at Santa Monica. Now, as well as the prospect of standing up in front of twenty thousand people, there was the looming moment when she would have to sit down and talk to Keith and the others. She hated letting people down and she hoped they wouldn't be too unhappy with her. Her anticipation increased as she counted down the days until Rob would return from the Far East. She had been thinking about him an awful lot and when he called her on Wednesday the thirtieth of November to report that he had arrived back in Italy and would be flying across to London on Friday just in time for the concert, she felt a wave of happiness sweep through her. If she had needed any proof of how much he now meant to her, this was more than enough.

With the concert imminent, Steph and the group spent hours at the huge O2 arena, rehearsing and watching the preparations being made to the stage and the intricately choreographed light show that would accompany the songs. This was also the first time she had seen Ethan since Italy, and she was delighted to find that he had stuck to his promise to moderate his drinking and steer clear of drugs, and he looked all the better for it. Although he once again looked and sounded presentable, she knew deep down that Rob had now irrevocably replaced him in her affections. Still, they were able to chat amicably and the atmosphere between them wasn't strained.

A final running order for the different numbers they would perform, including an encore, was decided, and Ethan and the technical director prepared a detailed checklist for the lighting engineers as well as the camera operators, so that the individual performers could be highlighted when they were playing a particular part. It was intricate, highly professional, and a bit scary. Steph did her best to memorise what she had to do and hoped she wouldn't mess things up. She and the others checked and rechecked their instruments while the roadies ensured that the whole complicated series of amplifiers and speakers that would pump the music out to the audience were functioning perfectly. The concert had sold out within an hour of tickets going on sale in October, so it was going to be a full house of twenty thousand fans plus live streaming to millions around the globe. It promised to be noisy both on and off stage.

When the big day arrived, Steph was nervous; maybe not quite as nervous as at Santa Monica, but still apprehensive. She received a text from Rob half an hour before the start, telling her his flight had been delayed, but had now landed and he was on his way to the arena in a taxi, but not likely to get there in time to wish her well. He just added the usual showbiz idiom 'Break a leg'. She replied, telling him how much she was looking forward to being with him again. She was still thinking about him as she squeezed into the glitzy costume that Bexley had picked out for her. If she had been in any doubt as to the depth of her feelings for Rob, the fact that she was looking forward more to seeing him tonight than to her first official concert in the UK with this legendary band proved it. She had no doubts about her priorities: Rob was what she wanted above all.

As in Santa Monica, the performance started with the lights dimmed and she followed the others out onto the stage in readiness for the start. When they were all in position, Johnny set things off with his usual 'One, two, three, four' and as they launched into the first number, the spotlights bathed the stage in light, and the audience erupted into an explosion of screams and raucous applause. This time, now that the new album was out, they worked their way through all the new songs as well as a few old favourites and the show took well over two hours. Steph's various solo pieces were well received, and her newfound singing role also drew noisy applause from the crowd. For her part she thoroughly enjoyed herself and couldn't help a feeling of regret that this life might have to come to an end if Keith didn't agree to let her step back from the spotlight, even if the trade-off was being able to settle down with Rob. But it was the only way.

When they finally reached the end of the show, the audience bayed for more, and Keith led them into 'Summer Nights', the same number they had played as an encore at the last concert. As before, this started with a virtuoso performance by him as he produced his guitar solo. The crowd were shouting and screaming in appreciation and clapping in time to the music with their arms aloft and there was a real buzz about the place. But then, just as he reached the climax of the piece, when Steph and the others were about to join in, something unexpected happened. The guitar, his beloved silver Stratocaster, slid from his hands and hung limply around his neck as he fell to his knees and then keeled over sideways, crouched in a foetal position, his feet flailing uncontrollably. The crowd roared, but Steph could see at once that something was seriously wrong. She abandoned her piano and ran towards him. So did Ben, and she and he got to Keith at the same moment. Keith was mouthing gibberish, his eyes staring unseeing up towards the roof. Ben saw at once what was happening.

'He's having a heart attack or a stroke.' He turned towards the wings and shouted at the top of his voice, only just audible over the racket coming from the crowd. 'Get help. Now!'

–

The newspapers next morning led with the story. The headlines spoke for themselves: *Rock Star Suffers Stroke on Stage* or the more populist *Keith Struck Down* and *Royalty Brought to its Knees*. Even *The Times* reported it at the bottom of the front page: *Keith Bailey (59) leader of world-famous band, Royalty, in critical condition after collapsing on stage.*

Steph scanned through the article before dropping the paper back on the table and picking up the lukewarm cup of black coffee Rob had brought her from the hospital cafeteria. It was just after nine o'clock in the morning and she hadn't slept in over twenty-four hours, but she was determined to stay with Faye and Rob and show solidarity for as long as it would take. Behind the closed doors of the ICU, she knew that medics were working feverishly to save Keith's life. Out here, Ben and Johnny were dozing, and Steph sat on one side of Faye with Rob positioned on the other side, both of them doing their best to comfort her. From time to time Steph caught Rob's eye, but she had hardly had a chance to exchange more than a few words with him since his father's collapse.

Her phone buzzed and she saw that it was Sky. As Faye had been barely coherent, racked with worry, Steph had called her and Denver while the paramedics were still working on Keith at the venue, and she was fielding their calls now.

'Hi, Sky, still no news, I'm afraid.'

'How's Mum bearing up?'

'It's a struggle but she's coping. Rob's looking after her. We're all together here at the hospital. Don't worry, I'll stay with her until they tell us he's all right.'

'And do they think he will be all right? It's been, what, almost twelve hours since it happened, hasn't it?'

Steph was just glancing at her watch when the door opposite opened, and a doctor came out and headed over towards them. She muttered a few words to Sky and turned her phone on to speaker, before taking Faye's arm as she got to her feet. The doctor pulled down his mask and addressed himself to Faye.

'Mrs Bailey? I'm pleased to report that your husband's doing better. He needs to rest, so we're going to keep him sedated for a day or two. I think you should go home and get some sleep. We've got your contact details. We'll call you when it's time to come and see him.'

Faye let out a massive sigh of relief and Rob spoke for her. 'Is he going to be all right? I mean, is he going to live?'

The doctor nodded. 'Yes, we're confident now that he'll live, although it was touch and go for a while. As for the final prognosis, we probably won't know for a few days. For now, it looks as though the left side of his body is partially paralysed, but that might be just a temporary phenomenon. Like I say, we'll know better in a little while, but the important thing is that he's out of danger.'

'Can I go in to see him?' Faye finally managed to find her voice.

'It's best if you don't, Mrs Bailey. He's heavily sedated and likely to stay that way for twelve, maybe twenty-four hours. He wouldn't even register that you're here. Take my advice. Go home and get some sleep.'

Faye mumbled a few words of thanks that Rob, Steph and the others echoed, and the doctor returned to his work. Steph glanced across at Ben and Johnny and heard Ben's voice. 'Faye, sweetie, do as the doc says. We'll call a cab right now to take us back to the hotel. We all need to get some sleep. You heard the doc; Keith's going to be okay.'

'But paralysed, that's what the doctor said.'

Steph was quick to reassure her. 'He didn't say that, Faye. He said the left side was partially paralysed at the moment, but everybody knows that strokes do that to people and he said it might well be temporary. It might take a bit of time, but he'll be okay again, I'm sure.'

Rob was still holding his mother's arm and he gently led her towards the door. Steph followed on with the others. Remembering she still had Sky on the line, she relayed the good news to her in case she hadn't heard the doctor, and on the way back to the hotel through the traffic she called Denver and repeated what the doctor had said. Sky had dropped everything and was already on the early morning train to London, although Denver was in the US and just sent his love. When Steph relayed the message to Faye that her daughter was coming, she looked pleased, if apprehensive.

'I just hope she'll find her father in good health.' She turned towards Steph and wiped away a tear. 'When the paramedics carried him off the stage, I honestly thought he was dead. Thank you, love, for all your support.' She looked over at Ben and Johnny. 'And thanks to you guys for staying with me.'

Ben reached out and caught hold of her hand. 'Always, Faye. We'll always be here for you and Keith. Now, try not to worry.'

Understandably, Rob stayed with his mother for the rest of the morning until his sister arrived to take over. It was three o'clock in the afternoon when Steph was woken by the arrival of a text from him.

> You awake? I need food. Feel like a late lunch? Mum and Sky are going to stay in their room and have room service, but I want to see you. x

Steph had no hesitation.

> Give me ten minutes to have a shower and change and I'll be ready. I'm in room 507. xx

She had just finished getting dressed when there was a tap at the door and she hurried across to open it. She caught hold of his hands, tugged him into the room, and kissed

298

him as if her very life depended on it. Finally she opened her eyes and stared at him from close quarters.

'I've missed you, Robert Bailey, I've missed you a lot.'

'And I've missed you, too, Stephanie Zanin, more than you can imagine.'

Chapter 27

The band meeting took place almost exactly a week later at Keith and Faye's house in Oxfordshire. Steph rented a car for the occasion and was glad of the satnav to direct her to a pair of anonymous wooden gates in the middle of thick woods bordering a country lane to the north of Woodstock. She pressed the buzzer and seconds later saw the gates begin to open. She drove in along a narrow drive that snaked through luxuriant rhododendron bushes two or three times taller than the car, before these gave way to a broad parking area in front of a charming old country house. She heard barking from inside and was met at the door by Faye and a pair of black Labradors. Steph hadn't seen Faye for five days and she was pleased to see her looking a bit less stressed than the last time they had been together.

'Hi, Faye. Hope I'm not late.'

Faye enveloped her in a warm hug. 'Hi, Steph, thanks for coming. Lottie and Ben are already here. We're just waiting for Johnny and Tara.' Faye led her inside with the dogs trotting alongside them, and Steph had to ask.

'Any relation to Waldorf?'

This raised a little smile on Faye's careworn face. 'Yes, indeed; mum and dad. Can you see the family resemblance?'

Steph bent down to pet them and saw the same lazy wag of the tail and the big brown eyes as her four-legged friend back in Italy.

Ben and Lottie were waiting in a magnificent old conservatory dotted with palms and orange and lemon trees like something out of Kew Gardens. In the middle of the room at one end of a low coffee table was Keith, and Steph swallowed hard as her eyes landed on him. He was in a wheelchair, his legs covered by a plaid blanket, and his previously tanned face was the colour of alabaster. Doing her best to conceal her concern and an overwhelming feeling of pity, she plastered on a smile and went over to give him a hug and a kiss.

'Hi, Keith, it's good to see you out of that hospital bed.' As she leant towards him she could see that the left-hand side of his face had sagged visibly and when he replied, she struggled to make out his words.

'Hi, Steph. Good of you to come. Take a seat.' She could see the effort it was costing him to string his words together.

Steph sat down on a wicker sofa with Lottie and Ben. The two dogs flopped down next to Keith while a friendly-looking lady came in to ask if anybody would like a coffee. She returned a couple of minutes later with coffees and a big plate of biscuits, which immediately attracted the dogs' attention, just as they would have done Waldorf's. The sound of a bell brought a volley of barking from the Labradors, who charged out of the door, followed at a more sedate pace by Faye. A minute later she returned accompanied by Johnny and Tara.

The band was complete.

Faye took a seat alongside her husband and looked on as Keith started the meeting. From time to time she helped him when words didn't come easily, and she occasionally wiped the side of his mouth with a tissue as he dribbled a little. Steph had a hard job not bursting into tears as she saw what he had now become. Compared to the dynamic, active man of barely a week ago, he was a shadow of his former self.

'Thanks, guys, it's good to see you all.' His speech was slurred but comprehensible.

Johnny didn't mince his words. 'It's damn good to see you alive, Keith. You had us all worried back there.'

There might even have been the hint of a smile on Keith's face for a fraction of a second before he replied. 'You weren't the only one, Johnny, but they tell me they think I'm not going to die just yet. Listen guys, we've got a big decision to make.'

He didn't need to spell it out. Steph knew what needed to be addressed and she was sure the others felt the same way. It was quite simply the future – or otherwise – of Royalty.

'The doctors tell me it's going to be a long haul. I'm starting on an intensive course of physiotherapy, but they've warned me not to expect an immediate improvement.' Keith paused before delivering the bad news, and they could all hear the emotion in his voice. 'In fact, they've warned me that there might be no improvement at all.' He looked around at them, the anguish in his eyes all too clear. 'I may never pick up a guitar again.'

'Don't say that, Keith. It's still early days. Give it time.' Ben was quick to offer reassurance and the others all joined in, but Keith waved them away weakly with his right hand.

'We've got to accept the facts, guys. It was a serious stroke – so serious it almost killed me – and it's probably going to be many months or even years before I get back to some sort of normality, if at all. What that means is that we need to make the big decision: what happens to Royalty?'

The others all looked at each other for a moment or two before Ben spoke up. 'Listen, Keith, I've been thinking, and one thing's crystal clear: Royalty without you makes no sense.'

Keith shook his head. 'Nobody's indispensable, Ben. There are some great guitar players out there. Just like Steph came along and replaced Vince so perfectly, you could find a replacement for me. I think we… you owe it to the fans to keep going.'

'I don't buy it. You aren't just lead guitar; you've written most of the songs, you've always been the leader on stage and off – and you pissed us off a fair bit while you were at it – but you and Royalty are one and the same. It's unthinkable to have the band without you.'

Johnny added his voice to Ben's argument. 'I'm with Ben on this. We're none of us getting any younger, Keith. Let's face it; none of us needs the money any more. We've got more than enough to see us out. The new album's getting great reviews and that concert last week was one of the best gigs we've ever done. I say let's sit back and wait for you to recover, and if you don't, we'll at least know we've gone out on a high.'

Keith took a few moments to weigh up his response. 'So you're saying we pull the plug on Royalty?'

'Not pull the plug – just put it on hold for now.' Johnny looked convinced. 'What does Sol say?'

'You can probably guess. He feels Royalty should carry on with or without me. If I can't play, you get a replacement. I can't say I blame him; we do represent a huge part of their turnover.'

'Yeah, but we've been effectively shut down for the last ten years and they've kept going all the same and made a whole heap of money out of our records. They've got a load of other artists. If we decide to walk away, they'll survive.'

Keith nodded a couple of times. 'What about Steph? She needs to have a say in this.' The three men looked across at her. 'You've only just joined the band, Steph. It's unfair for us to do you out of what would have been a hugely successful career. If we do as Ben and Johnny are saying, you're going to find yourself out of a job for months, years, maybe forever. If you guys find a replacement for me and let Royalty carry on like Sol wants, the sky's the limit for somebody with your talent. What do *you* think we should do?'

Steph replied immediately. She had been thinking about this over and over again in the course of the week and she threw in her weight alongside the other band members, feeling sure that this was the very best solution not just for Keith, but for her personally.

'If you want my opinion, I know Royalty will go on forever. Music's like literature: Shakespeare's been dead for five hundred years, but we all still know him and his work, and his plays are still performed all around the globe. It's the same with music. Look at Mozart: he died over two hundred years ago but his music lives on and his name's more famous now than it ever was when he was alive. I'm delighted and honoured to have contributed to the recent album, but I agree with Johnny and Ben; there's no way you could or should ever be replaced. Like the others say, do what you three did ten years ago after Vince's death:

put Royalty on hold and see how we all feel in a year, five, ten years' time. I'm confident you'll regain the use of your arm, and you'll start playing again and when you do, we'll be with you. Even if you can't play properly for now, you can still keep writing songs and when you feel up to it, we can get back together and start up again. No Keith, no Royalty.'

She saw Faye shoot a grateful smile at her and that same hint of a smile appeared on Keith's face before he had one more try. 'But that'll mean you'll be out of a job.'

Steph beamed at him. 'That's not going to be a problem. I've already had another job offer.'

All eyes in the room turned back towards her in amazement and Steph savoured the moment for a few seconds before explaining. 'Rob's been looking for an accompanist and he thinks I'd be up to it. I can't think of anything better.'

Faye's eyes lit up. 'Does that mean you'd move to Italy?'

'Your son's very kindly offered me a place in his house.'

'You're moving in together? Isn't that a bit soon?' Keith looked surprised but not displeased.

'That's what I said to him, but he was adamant. As for me, I just know it's the right thing to do.'

The delight on Faye's face was a joy to see and there were tears in her eyes as she turned towards her husband and caught hold of his hand. 'After everything that's happened over the last few days, I can't imagine better news.' The tears started running down her cheeks as she looked back across the room. 'Steph, sweetheart, you've no idea how happy that makes me feel. Right, Keith?'

This time there was definitely more than a hint of a smile on Keith's face.

Epilogue

Steph flew across to Pisa next morning and took the train up to Sarzana. She deliberately hadn't told Rob she was coming as she wanted to surprise him, so she took a taxi and got the driver to drop her at the start of the gravel track so she could walk up to his house. It was a cold, dry day and the air was so clear she could make out the individual houses on the hillside far away on the north side of the Gulf of the Poets. All around her the olive trees were strung with netting to catch the falling fruit and it looked as though the olive harvest was in full swing. There was the familiar aroma of cypress resin in the air, and she breathed deeply. It all felt so familiar and so very welcoming. The smile that had been on her face most of the way over on the plane now broadened. It felt like coming home.

She had only just started lugging her suitcase towards the house when she was greeted by a familiar face. A large black shape came careering towards her and almost bowled her over, such was his delight to see her again.

'*Ciao, bello.*' She crouched down and made a fuss of the Labrador before straightening up and reaching for her suitcase again. A voice from among the olive trees stopped her.

'*Buongiorno, signora*, can I help you with that?' Rob emerged and caught hold of her hands, pulling her into his arms.

Steph stared lovingly up at him. 'Signor Sinclair? I'm Stephanie Zanin, I'd like to accept your kind offer of employment as your new accompanist.'

He grinned at her. 'I look forward to working with you, Ms Zanin. I'm sure you'll be perfect for the job. If you'd like to accompany me to the house, I have a grand piano waiting for you.' His grin broadened. 'You should have told me you were coming. I could have picked you up. Anyway, you're here now and that's all that matters. Can I offer you a coffee?'

'I'd like that very much.'

He picked up her suitcase and took hold of her hand with his free hand and they walked up the drive to the house together, the dog trotting happily ahead of them. As they walked, Rob turned his head towards her.

'How's Dad?'

'I was with him yesterday. He's recovering. It'll be a long process, but he'll get there, I'm sure.'

'And when he does, what then?' He caught her eye. 'For you, I mean?'

'I think we'll cross that bridge when we come to it. I'd love to think that your dad can make a full recovery and that Royalty can be resurrected once more, but that's all for the future. All I know is that I'm where I want to be for now. What was that you were saying about carpe diem?'

He stopped in the middle of the track and set down the suitcase. Turning towards her, he looked deep into her eyes. 'The thought of living with you and working with you is all I could ever have hoped for and more. I feel amazingly privileged.' His expression changed to one of insecurity. 'Are you sure I'm worth it?'

She leant forward and kissed him softly on the lips.

'You're worth it.' A movement at their feet made her look down. The Labrador had squeezed himself in between them and was staring up at them adoringly. She smiled down at him. 'Besides, it's not just you I want to be with.'

'Love me, love my dog?'

'Both of you. Forever.'

Acknowledgements

My warmest thanks to my editor at Canelo, Emily Bedford, who always makes the right suggestions. Thanks also to the whole team at Canelo, who do a wonderful job.

Never Too Late

T.A. Williams lives in Devon with his Italian wife. He was born in England of a Scottish mother and Welsh father. After a degree in modern languages at Nottingham University, he lived and worked in Switzerland, France and Italy, before returning to run one of the best-known language schools in the UK. He's taught Arab princes, Brazilian beauty queens and Italian billionaires. He speaks a number of languages and has travelled extensively. He has eaten snake, still-alive fish, and alligator. A Spanish dog, a Russian bug and a Korean parasite have done their best to eat him in return. His hobby is long-distance cycling, but his passion is writing.

Also by T.A. Williams

Chasing Shadows
Dreaming of Venice
Dreaming of Florence
Dreaming of St-Tropez
Dreaming of Christmas
Dreaming of Tuscany
Dreaming of Rome
Dreaming of Verona
Dreaming of Italy

Escape to Tuscany

Under a Siena Sun
Second Chances in Chianti
Secrets on the Italian Island

Love from Italy

A Little Piece of Paradise
An Escape to Remember
A Chance in a Million

Beneath Italian Skies

Never Too Late